SCIENCE MATTERS

Insulin: Discovery and Development

prepared for the Course Team
by Jeff Thomas

GW00992275

Science: a second level course

The S280 Course Team

Pam Berry (Text Processing)

Norman Cohen (Author)

Angela Colling (Author)

Michael Gillman (Author)

John Greenwood (Librarian)

Barbara Hodgson (Reader)

David Johnson (Author)

Carol Johnstone (Course Secretary)

Hilary MacQueen (Author)

Isla McTaggart (Course Manager)

Diane Mole (Designer)

Joanna Munnelly (Editor)

Pat Murphy (Author)

Ian Nuttall (Editor)

Pam Owen (Graphic Artist)

Malcolm Scott (Author)

Sandy Smith (Author)

Margaret Swithenby (Editor)

Jeff Thomas (Course Team Chair and Author)

Kiki Warr (Author)

Bill Young (BBC Producer)

External Assessor: John Durant

The Open University, Walton Hall, Milton Keynes, MK7 6AA.

First published 1993.

Edited, designed and typeset in the United Kingdom by the Open University.

Printed in the United Kingdom by Eyre & Spottiswoode Ltd, Margate, Kent.

ISBN 07492 51085

This text forms part of an Open University Second Level Course. If you would like a copy of *Studying with the Open University*, please write to the Central Enquiry Service, PO Box 200, The Open University, Walton Hall, Milton Keynes, MK 7 6YZ. If you have not already enrolled on the Course and would like to buy this or other Open University material, please write to Open University Educational Enterprises Ltd, 12 Cofferidge Close, Stony Stratford, Milton Keynes, MK11 1BY, United Kingdom.

1.1

6390C/s280iddi1.1

Contents

1 Introduction

The focus of this book is the protein **insulin**, a hormone known to be vitally important for human health. The disease **diabetes** arises when insulin fails to do its job properly in the human body. As you will see, our understanding of the physiological role of insulin has increased enormously since its discovery more than 70 years ago, allowing the development of methods of successfully treating diabetes.

Chapter 2 describes the events that led up to the discovery of insulin, culminating with its 'miraculous' use in restoring to good health patients on the brink of death. This dramatic episode has been well researched, notably by the scientific historian Michael Bliss in his book *The Discovery of Insulin*, so we are in the happy and unusual position of knowing how this new scientific understanding came about, as well as knowing a good deal about the personal ambitions and conflicts that accompanied it. In describing these particular events, the aim here is to illustrate an important general principle, which is that, contrary to popular belief, science moves forward by a process very different from the mechanical and dispassionate collection of dry facts in a social vacuum.

Chapter 2 reveals how slow and uncertain was the road to the discovery of insulin in the 1920s. By contrast, Chapter 3 reveals that research and development in the field of insulin and diabetes has been very rapid and productive in modern times. Medical advances have ensured a reasonably healthy and normal life for hundreds of thousands of patients world-wide who are dependent upon daily doses of insulin. At some unknown time in the future, a continuation of the same processes should bring within reach a cure for diabetes. In an era in which science-based issues are often a source of public anxiety, it is fitting to also be made aware of one of the many benevolent roles of modern science.

2 Discovery

Had you lived before the 20th century and developed diabetes, you would have faced the prospect of increasing lethargy, gradual wastage and certain premature death. This distressing condition probably contributed to human misery on a major scale even before its first documented appearance in 1550 BC, when it was described as the disease of 'overabundant urine'. More crudely, a 17th century English physician termed the disease 'the pissing evile'. Historically, 'treatment' of the disease often involved therapies as bizarre as they were ineffective; including bleeding, a diet of potatoes and excessive feeding of sugar, which often did little more than hasten death.

The major symptoms of diabetes were described accurately almost 2 000 years ago by Arataeus of Cappadocia (now Central Turkey) who first coined the word diabetes, from the Greek, meaning 'to run through a syphon'. He applied the term indiscriminately to all conditions involving excessive production of urine and left us a vivid and accurate clinical description of the disease:

> *Diabetes is a dreadful affliction, not very frequent among men, being a melting down of the flesh and limbs into urine. The patients never stop making water and the flow is incessant, like the opening of aqueducts. Life is short, unpleasant and painful, thirst unquenchable, drinking excessive and disproportionate to the large quantity of urine, for yet more urine is passed.*

Ancient physicians also learnt that the urine of people with diabetes was often sweet to the taste, which accounts for the modern term for the commonest form of the disease—diabetes *mellitus* (from the Latin word for honey). However, an understanding of the origins of 'the pissing evile' had to wait until the early 19th century. At that time, it became firmly established, by careful observations and by experiment, that the condition was not primarily attributable, as Arataeus had supposed, to a malfunction of the kidneys—which as you know are the sites of urine production—but to problems with the **pancreas**.

The extraction of insulin from the pancreas in the early 1920s identified one of the first of many **hormones** ('chemical messengers') that we now know play a vital role in the regulation of the body's functions. This discovery revolutionized the treatment of diabetes and undoubtedly represents a milestone in medical science. It would be heartening, therefore, to claim that the discovery of insulin was a triumph for the methodical application of scientific analysis, in the best traditions of painstaking and selfless endeavour. The true story is a much more touching and revealing saga, showing, with all the clarity and drama of a comic opera, that the progress of science is no more perfect an activity than other human endeavours.

To get the most from the story we first need to jump ahead and say something in the next section about our *present-day* knowledge of diabetes and its causes. You may well be familiar with some of this background already, so we will cover the ground at a relatively brisk pace.

2.1 The biological background

The human pancreas is situated close to the much more sizeable liver, and its unremarkable appearance and size give little clue to its important functions. Figure 2.1a shows, in a highly schematic way, what we now know of its detailed internal structure. The main bulk of the organ consists of two different types of cell groups; for clarity, the diagram shows only a few of each type. The more numerous groups of cells secrete a solution containing a range of digestive enzymes, which, after passing along a series of narrow ducts and eventually into the more substantial **pancreatic duct**, are conveyed into the intestine. This secretion is often termed the **external secretion** of the pancreas.

▷   What function do the enzymes of this secretion perform in the intestine?

▶   As digestive enzymes, they ensure the chemical breakdown of foodstuffs, notably proteins, fats and carbohydrates.

Interspersed in the main mass of enzyme-producing pancreatic cells, in a manner that reminded early microscopists of islands scattered in a sea, are separate clusters of a second cell type, which produce an **internal secretion** (see Figure 2.1a and b and Plates 2.1a and b). We now know that *insulin* is a major constituent of this secretion. As you can appreciate from Figure 2.1a, this hormone exerts an influence around the entire body, since it is conveyed from the pancreas via the bloodstream, *not* via the pancreatic duct.

Once the insulin is released via this route from the pancreas, its main effect is to *remove* **glucose** *from the blood*. You will already know something of the central

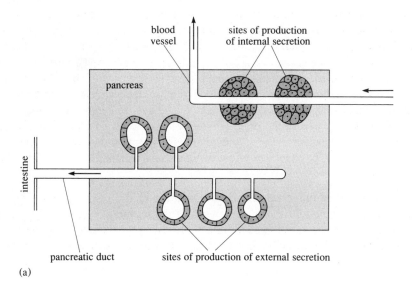

(a)

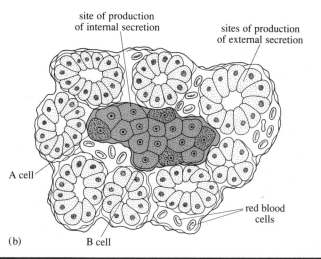

(b)

Figure 2.1   (a) Schematic diagram of the microscopic structure of the human pancreas. For clarity, only a few groups of each cell type are shown. (b) Simplified anatomical drawing of a microscopic section of a small representative portion of pancreatic tissue (magnified about 200 times). A single cell group responsible for the internal secretion is shown in pink, surrounded by several cell groups producing external secretion. You will learn about cell types A and B in Section 3.1.2. (The *actual* microscopic appearance of the pancreas is shown in Plate 2.1.)

importance of glucose as a basic fuel for metabolism; it is a key raw material because its oxidation yields supplies of **ATP**, adenosine triphosphate, which is the standard 'currency' of metabolic energy. Of course, glucose is not the *only* metabolic fuel of the body—the oxidation of fatty acids provides a particularly important source of ATP. However, there are a number of key tissues (in particular, the brain, red blood cells and the kidney) that cannot use any fuel other than glucose to a significant degree. Wherever and whenever cells do anything that requires energy, such as synthesize complex chemicals, divide, actively transport solutes from outside the cell into the interior, secrete macromolecules or move about, ATP is utilized. The amounts of ATP that cells can store internally and therefore have at their immediate disposal are very limited, so most cells need a continuous supply of glucose, either for immediate oxidation or for temporary storage (in the form of **glycogen**, which is a polymer of glucose).

The digestion of carbohydrate foodstuffs in the intestine (partly by the enzymes in the external secretion of the pancreas) yields a large amount of glucose, which is then absorbed into the intestinal bloodstream, for eventual delivery to all living cells throughout the body. When the body requires fuel in large quantities, for example during exercise, tissues soon use up internal stores and then have to rely on glucose from the blood. Blood glucose levels therefore fall, normally to be restored by glucose produced via the breakdown of glycogen (especially that in the liver); glycogen is therefore normally metabolized when fuel demands in the body are high.

Only a limited range of concentrations of blood glucose can be tolerated by the body, largely because the cells of the brain seem especially sensitive to the substance. Low blood glucose levels, a condition known as **hypoglycaemia**, lead to drowsiness, headache, loss of concentration and, if the condition is severe and persistent, to convulsions and life-threatening coma; these are the consequences of the brain being starved of its fuel supply. An excess of blood glucose, technically termed **hyperglycaemia**, can also cause a dangerous coma, but this is less common and less risky than hypoglycaemia because the brain is more tolerant of raised blood sugar levels. As we shall see in Chapter 3, early symptoms normally provide diabetic patients with an important warning of excessively low or high blood glucose levels, which allows remedial action.

We now know that insulin removes glucose from the bloodstream by promoting its uptake by cells, notably those of the liver and of the muscles. Very small amounts of the hormone are released continuously in a slight trickle of internal secretion from the pancreas, called the *basal* secretion, but when circumstances demand it, insulin release is dramatically boosted.

▷   When would enhanced insulin release from the pancreas be most advantageous—well before or soon after a meal?

▶   Soon after a meal, when blood glucose levels are increasing. Insulin release would prevent hyperglycaemia and help 'load up' cells with glucose, to be oxidized immediately or stored temporarily in the form of glycogen.

The periodic release of insulin is one of the key factors helping to maintain blood glucose levels in the healthy human at a more or less constant level. As mentioned above, blood glucose levels tend to increase following food intake; this elevation in blood glucose immediately stimulates the pancreas to release insulin into the bloodstream, which promotes the uptake of glucose into cells, which then reduces blood glucose levels, restoring values closer to pre-meal levels. When normal blood glucose levels are eventually restored, insulin release from the pancreas is very sharply reduced.

This last point reveals the form of control that is at work here: the restoration of normal blood glucose levels is a signal which 'feeds back' to an earlier stage in the system to influence output, in this case to sharply reduce insulin secretion. It is an example of **negative feedback**, a process which is sometimes called **closed-loop control**, for reasons that Activity 2.1 will make clear.

Activity 2.1

A flow chart is a useful way of summarizing and helping to remember a chain of events such as that just described. To be effective a flow chart needs to be simple, use very short descriptions and concentrate only on major events.

Draw a flow chart, consisting of a series of labelled boxes linked by arrows, to summarize the sequence of key events described so far in Section 2.1 involving glucose and insulin, starting with the ingestion of carbohydrate-rich food. How might the negative feedback involved be shown on your flow chart?

The fact that insulin release from the pancreas is influenced by the glucose level in the blood is particularly important. Remember that insulin secretion is *increased* significantly by raised glucose levels in the blood and *reduced* sharply by a lowering of blood glucose levels.

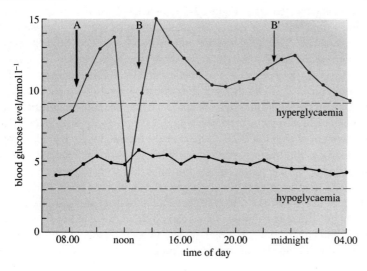

Figure 2.2 Blood glucose levels in two individuals, one normal (black line) and one diabetic (continuous red line) over 24 hours. Insulin was self-administered by the diabetic individual at the times shown by the vertical arrows, in large (A) or small (B and B') doses. Blood glucose levels marking the approximate thresholds for the onset of hypoglycaemia and hyperglycaemia are shown as dashed red lines.

Activity 2.2   *You should spend up to 20 minutes on this activity.*

Figure 2.2 shows the levels of glucose in the blood samples removed at hourly intervals from two individuals over a 24-hour period. First, consider the black line, showing glucose levels in a *non-diabetic* individual during a typical daily routine.

(a) Estimate the times when breakfast and lunch were consumed.

(b) Estimate the times at which insulin secretion above the basal level is likely to have begun. What factor is likely to have initiated this insulin release?

(c) A late snack was taken at about 21.00. Offer a plausible reason for its limited effect on blood glucose levels.

By contrast, the red line in Figure 2.2 shows the blood glucose levels in a moderately diabetic individual, eating identical meals at the same times of day as the non-diabetic individual. The vertical arrows show the times when the patient injected two different-size doses of insulin.

(d) Figure 2.2 shows that the average blood glucose level is higher in the diabetic than in the non-diabetic individual. It also shows that the increases in blood glucose levels after consuming food are more rapid and more substantial in the diabetic than in the non-diabetic individual. Are these two observations consistent with the fact that this diabetic patient is unable to secrete insulin from the pancreas? If so, explain why.

(e) Describe and explain the effects of injected insulin. In your answer mention (i) whether insulin has an immediate effect and (ii) the effects of the different-size doses of insulin.

The data in Figure 2.2 provide strong evidence that this form of diabetes can be attributed to insulin deficiency. (Later, in Chapter 3, you will see that another form of diabetes mellitus is not quite so easily explained.) This is readily checked by measuring the amount of insulin present in the blood of a normal individual and that of a diabetic person (see Figure 2.3).

What should be evident from Figure 2.3 is that increases in insulin concentration in the blood normally coincide roughly with meal times, which is much the same conclusion as we drew from Figure 2.2. But the implication of the red line in Figure 2.3 is that this particular diabetic individual cannot produce sufficient insulin 'on demand', suggesting that the insulin-producing cells of the pancreas are malfunctioning.

What is perhaps unexpected from Figure 2.3 is that levels of insulin in the blood of the healthy individual fall sharply between meals and rise sharply afterwards, giving the characteristic peaks. This suggests that after insulin secretion from the pancreas is 'turned down' (to the basal rate) via negative feedback, the insulin is removed from the bloodstream. (Remember that diabetic patients require successive injections of insulin; see Figure 2.2.) Cells that are responsive to insulin (i.e. the *target* cells), particularly those in the liver, muscles and fat deposits, contain **receptors** at the outer cell membrane, to which insulin becomes bound. (This binding is the first of a long chain of biochemical events that lead to increased glucose uptake into the target cells.) After insulin-binding, the insulin–receptor complex is taken into the cell and the insulin broken down. So the supply of the hormone has to be constantly replenished from the pancreas. If it were not, blood glucose levels would rise, as happens in diabetes. The fact that insulin is removed from the bloodstream is highly advantageous in terms of glucose control; if it remained there, it would carry on promoting glucose uptake and 'overshoot' the point where 'normal' levels of blood glucose were restored, with the resulting risk of hypoglycaemia.

▷   How might you investigate further the suggestion that diabetes is the result of insulin deficiency.

▶   One approach would be to look at the structure of the pancreas of diabetic individuals, to see if the insulin-producing cells are in some way different from those of non-diabetic individuals.

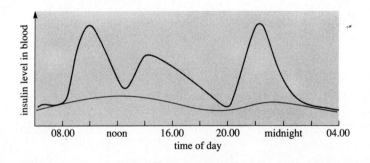

Figure 2.3   Changes in insulin levels in the blood of two individuals eating high-carbohydrate meals at the same times—about 7.45, noon and 20.00. The black line shows levels in a normal individual, the red line that in a diabetic person. The units in which insulin is measured in the blood need not concern us, so the vertical axis has no scale.

The cells of the pancreas that produce internal secretion are readily distinguished using standard staining techniques (see Plate 2.1a). More specific techniques can nowadays identify particular hormones. Plates 2.1b and c show photographs of different microscopic sections of pancreatic tissue, 'stained' in different ways to show up insulin; in (b), discrete 'islands' of densely staining cells are visible. In the normal pancreas (Plate 2.1c), the majority of the cells producing internal secretion display stain that is specific for insulin (dark brown areas). This staining is absent from such cells in the pancreas of a diabetic patient (Plate 2.1d).

In diabetes mellitus there is a major upset in the body's handling of carbohydrate fuel. As Figure 2.2 showed, levels of blood glucose are raised substantially—the condition of hyperglycaemia. The urine of a non-diabetic individual has a very low glucose concentration. This is because the kidneys are normally able to reclaim nearly all the glucose initially extracted from the blood during the first stages of urine formation; in diabetes, so much glucose is present in the blood that the capacity of the kidneys is exceeded, with the result that much of the glucose cannot be reclaimed and therefore appears in the urine—a condition known as **glycosuria**. For reasons that we need not explore here, the kidney's usual ability to pass relatively modest volumes of urine is upset by the presence of excess glucose, resulting in the formation of large volumes of a dilute urine. This, in turn, causes dehydration in the body, which leads to rampant thirst. Because glucose is no longer available to the cells that need it, the energy demands of the body have to be met from alternative sources. So other potential fuels in the body's tissues, such as stored fats and muscle proteins, are turned to, which is a major reason for the resulting rapid loss of body mass. Without the benefit of knowing the underlying cause, Arataeus described the outward appearance of the sad process well: the 'melting down of the flesh and limbs into urine'.

2.2 The moments of discovery

Scientific discoveries are commonly portrayed as imaginative leaps in the dark, where divine inspiration, meticulous planning and unshakable clarity of scientific thought combine magically to shed light and understanding. Most discoveries are shaped by more down-to-earth factors, and even the greatest discoverers would admit that the seeds of revelation were laid by the work of their forebears. The discoverers of insulin in 1922 certainly owed a debt to previous workers, so at this point we should look at what was known about diabetes early in the 20th century.

As already mentioned, the major symptoms of diabetes were well established— excess, sugary, urine and constant thirst. Something of the detailed structure of the pancreas was known; in 1869 Paul Langerhans, a German medical student, had discovered that the pancreas consisted of the two types of cell groups identified in Figure 2.1; several years later, the less numerous islands of cells, which we now know to be the source of the internal secretion of the pancreas, were termed the **Islets of Langerhans**, in honour of the discoverer.

At that time, the function of the Islet cells was uncertain and indeed the relationship between diabetes and the pancreas was yet to be established. One of the early pieces in the jigsaw puzzle was inadvertently supplied in 1889 by Oskar Minkowski, Professor of Medicine at Strasbourg, who was concerned to establish whether the pancreas produced the digestive enzymes that were essential to the breakdown of fats in the intestine. His approach, in an era less troubled by the ethics of animal experimentation, was to remove the entire pancreas of a dog; as a result, the depancreatized animal indeed digested fats less completely—it is now well established that external secretion from the pancreas contains lipases (fat-splitting enzymes). But of greater relevance to our present context, the dog developed the typical symptoms of diabetes.

▷ Had you been in Minkowski's shoes, what conclusion in relation to the cause of diabetes would you have drawn from this experiment?

▶ That the absence of the pancreas causes diabetes, or to put it the other way round, a healthy pancreas keeps diabetes at bay.

▷ But could there be other explanations, suggesting that **control experiments** are needed?

▶ Yes. Minkowski's experiment inevitably involved more than simply removing the pancreas—anaesthetics were applied, incisions were made, blood was lost—any one of these unnatural events could, perhaps, have triggered diabetes. For these reasons, control experiments would nowadays be conducted—including what are normally termed **sham operations**, identical in every respect to the actual operation, except that in this case the pancreas would *not* be removed.

Minkowski's chance observation encouraged him to question the source of the 'anti-diabetic' factor. Perhaps it was contained within the pancreatic secretion that he knew was secreted into the intestine. His method of directly testing this was either to cut the pancreatic duct or to tie it off with thread, a technique called **ligation**; both methods would interrupt the flow of external secretion.

▷ On the basis of the information in Section 2.1, is it likely that such procedures would have led to diabetes?

▶ No, because we now know that insulin from the Islets of Langerhans passes into the bloodstream, not into the intestine (Figure 2.1a).

Indeed, dogs with ligated pancreatic ducts did not develop diabetes; only the removal of the entire pancreas caused the condition to arise. Furthermore, when pancreatic tissue was transplanted from a healthy dog into a diabetic animal, the symptoms of the disease in the recipient disappeared. Minkowski thus was the first to appreciate the dual function of the pancreas—producing both an external secretion aiding digestion, and an internal secretion of 'something' implicated in carbohydrate metabolism and essential for the avoidance of diabetes. The suggestion that this unknown something emanated from the Islets of Langerhans came a few years later, mainly on the evidence of the unusual microscopic appearance of the Islet cells in the pancreas of human diabetic patients at post-mortem examination; such cells were often shrunken and distorted (see Plate 2.1d). The logical conclusion was that the Islet cells produced the anti-diabetic factor and in 1916 this hypothesized component of the internal secretion was named insulin, after the Latin *insula*, an island. Insulin has the distinction of being a hormone whose existence was hypothesized before its discovery.

By this stage, the hunt was on for an effective method of treating diabetes by administering *extracts* of the pancreas containing this hormone. The Islets were under suspicion as the sites of insulin production, but separating them out from the remaining pancreatic tissue was at that time far too tricky. So the general approach was to mince up the entire pancreas in one or more solvents, following a range of different procedures, and then to administer various forms of the filtered extract to diabetic patients or animals, either by injection or by mouth. The volume and sugar content of the urine was usually then measured to establish the effects. About 400 research workers were probably engaged world-wide in the task, at a time when the Islets probably enjoyed temporarily the status of 'most studied tissue of the human body'; initially these Herculean efforts produced little more than confusion and disappointment. Some extracts did lower the sugar content of urine, for shorter or longer periods, and some had no effect; others had harmful effects, inducing fever, shock or collapse. Though some workers came close, notably Kleiner of the Rockefeller Institute in New York and Paulesco in Bucharest, none could fulfil all the necessary criteria for success—namely obtaining consistently positive results with administered extracts, with no substantial ill-effect on the recipients, and acceptable to scientific contemporaries. With such lack of success, early expressions of optimism began to be replaced by doubt, not so much about the existence of a pancreatic hormone with anti-diabetic properties but about the feasibility of extracting it and using it therapeutically. It was against such an uncertain background that the Canadian researchers Banting and Best began their work on pancreatic extracts in 1921.

2.2.1 'A stronghold of truth'

By all accounts, Frederick Banting was shy, insecure and temperamental by nature—qualities that, as we shall see, generated a great capacity for both anger and ambition. His medical training started in Toronto, Canada, to be followed by a brief and undistinguished spell of study in England and then rather more eventfully as a medical officer in the last year of the First World War. Active service at the front line provided vivid and extensive experience of surgery, but his career ambitions in that direction were thwarted, and on his return to Canada he was obliged to set up in general practice in London, Ontario. Much to his regret, he was launched on a career as a struggling 'country doctor', filling in time with some teaching at a local university.

In his preparation for classes on carbohydrate metabolism, Banting was prompted to find out more about diabetes, a subject in which he had hitherto expressed no particular interest. He read a routine research article reporting an unusual occurrence that the author, Moses Barron, had observed in a human pancreas at post-mortem; minerals and organic material had accumulated to form a 'stone', which had blocked the pancreatic duct. Most of the cells of the pancreas producing the external secretion (see Figure 2.1) had died away, while the cells of the Islets of Langerhans appeared to be largely intact. Barron pointed out that much the same result had been reported by research workers who had experimentally tied (i.e. ligated) the pancreatic duct. A pancreas affected in this way, either naturally or by experiment, was termed **degenerate**, reflecting the fact that it was unable to function normally, at least with respect to its external secretion.

It is uncertain whether Barron's interpretation was in fact correct—the patient was diabetic and it was therefore more than likely that the Islet tissue *had* been damaged by the pancreatic duct obstruction—but this dubious report sparked off a 'great idea' in Banting's mind. Banting formed a hypothesis to explain why extraction of insulin from the pancreas had up to that time been so problematic; during the extraction process, the powerful digestive enzymes within the external secretion had destroyed the proposed anti-diabetic hormone within the internal secretion. Perhaps ligation of the pancreatic duct, and the resulting destruction of the digestive-enzyme-producing cells in such a degenerate pancreas, would mean the internal secretion was 'there for the taking'.

Inspiration led to action. Banting immediately contrived an introduction to the Professor of Physiology at the University of Toronto, John Macleod. Macleod was

Figure 2.4 Charles Best (left) and Frederick Banting (right) in 1921 with Marjorie, one of the few dogs in that year to have undergone successful surgery. The pancreas had been removed and the animal thereafter kept alive by injection of pancreatic extracts.

a distinguished, somewhat austere and proud individual, with a well-established reputation in the field of carbohydrate metabolism. We can only guess at the strong reservations he very likely had about the wild and naive proposals put to him — Macleod knew, and no doubt told Banting, that many others had tried to extract insulin, without success, and others had investigated the effects of ligating the pancreatic duct. But none had apparently used the technique as a prelude to isolating the proposed hormone. So, Macleod agreed to provide the guidance and support that would allow Banting's experimental work to begin. Laboratory facilities and experimental animals were to be provided, as well as practical assistance in the form of a 'volunteer' from the final year class in Physiology and Biochemistry, Charles Best — who reputedly won the right to do so on the toss of a coin.

In May 1921, Banting and Best started experiments involving operations on dogs. As you will see, it is difficult to see how insulin could have been discovered in a way that did not involve animal experimentation. Figure 2.4 shows Banting and Best with one of their many experimental animals.

Despite Banting's surgical flair and help with the technique from the more experienced Macleod, ligation of the pancreatic duct proved technically difficult and did not always lead to the expected pancreatic degeneration. An early aim of Banting and Best was to inject an extract from a degenerate pancreas into the bloodstream of an animal from which the pancreas had previously been removed.

▷   Why was this an important experiment and what was the hoped-for outcome?

▶   If the pancreatic extract contained an anti-diabetic agent, diabetic symptoms in the depancreatized dog should diminish, i.e. the glucose content of the blood and urine should be lowered.

In reality, obtaining diabetic animals by removing the entire pancreas proved problematic, because the trauma of the operation often resulted in the death of the animal.

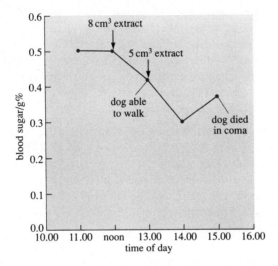

Figure 2.5 An example of Banting and Best's results showing the effects on blood sugar of injecting an extract of a degenerate pancreas into a depancreatized recipient. Blood sugar levels are here expressed in the now antiquated units of grams (g) of sugar per 100 cm³ of blood, commonly called g%. (Note that the techniques used at this time measured a range of glucose-like sugars in blood (and urine), hence the correct term here is 'blood sugar'; modern techniques are specific for glucose.)

Activity 2.3   *You should spend up to 20 minutes on this activity.*

Results from an early experiment are shown in Figure 2.5. Before the extract was injected, it was clear that this depancreatized dog was far from normal—Banting's laboratory notes suggest that the animal was in a coma, on the brink of death. Blood sugar levels were measured before and after two injections of extract into the bloodstream, at the times indicated.

(a) Why was it important to measure blood sugar level *before* the first injection?

(b) Do you think it is valid to conclude positively from these data that the effect of the extract is to lower blood sugar levels?

At the time, other reservations were expressed to Banting and Best, by Macleod for example. Some of these concerns and anomalies are highlighted in questions (c) and (d). For each question, think carefully about the information immediately preceding it, before you answer.

In some of Banting and Best's experiments, the impure extracts often evoked a powerful toxic response in the recipient animal, sometimes resulting in an immediate and strong fever. Perhaps the fall in blood sugar level was a consequence solely of the elevation of body temperature, rather than a direct effect of the extract itself.

(c) In general terms, can you think of a procedure that would exclude such a possibility?

Substantial volumes of extract (13 cm^3 in total in Figure 2.5) were injected into animals that have a total blood volume of about 700 cm^3.

(d) How could you exclude the possibility that the extract simply diluted the blood, and that this accounted for the fall in blood sugar concentration?

In later experiments, Banting and Best prepared extracts of whole 'fresh' pancreas immediately after its removal from normal dogs. Their experimental records show a *swift and substantial drop in blood sugar* on injection of such an extract, although they failed to draw proper conclusions from this significant observation at the time.

(e) Was this experimental result consistent with Banting's initial hypothesis?

So, on this evidence, Banting's initial inspired idea was faulty. In science, discarding a faulty hypothesis in the light of new information is a common enough event and no cause for shame. Progress comes when thoughts are revised and a new hypothesis is put forward that more closely fits the facts. Banting and Best took the alternative line, and stubbornly stuck to their original hypothesis, despite evidence to the contrary. Extracts were still routinely obtained using whole degenerate pancreas. Their published papers reiterated the 'ligation' hypothesis, despite the inclusion of results with fresh pancreas, which were presented without significant comment.

How much Macleod appreciated this anomaly is uncertain. He certainly pressed Banting and Best to improve both the quality and quantity of their data and persisted with a number of awkward questions. Had all of the pancreatic tissue been removed in the depancreatized dogs? Was the degenerate pancreatic tissue genuinely free of external secretion? How could one be certain that the observed fall in blood sugar was attributable to the injected internal secretion? A surviving note from Macleod gives an insight into his thinking:

> *You know that if you can prove to the satisfaction of everyone that such extracts really have the power to reduce blood sugar in pancreatic diabetes, you will have achieved a very great deal. Kleiner and others who have published somewhat similar results have not convinced others because their proofs were not adequate. It's very easy often in science to satisfy one's own self about some point but it is very hard to build up a stronghold of proof which others cannot pull down. Now supposing I wanted to be one of those critics I would say that your results on this particular dog are not absolutely convincing ...*

Banting mistook this proper scientific scepticism for hostility, feeling that Macleod was too dim and self-interested to see the strength and importance of his hard-won results. Some control experiments were conducted, but Banting rarely measured body temperature (see Activity 2.3c) despite the often toxic properties of the extract. It seems that much of Macleod's wise advice at the time was ignored.

Despite their muddled thinking and wrong guesses, some success had come Banting and Best's way—the experiments had at least set them on the right trail. But, as Macleod pointed out, at this point their work had gone no further than that of others, such as Kleiner in the USA, who had used pancreatic extracts to relieve diabetic symptoms in experimental animals. However, the Canadian work was soon to progress, despite a deteriorating atmosphere amongst the three colleagues, where suspicion and rivalry had begun to replace the initial euphoria and enthusiasm. Banting's fear was that Macleod was aiming to capture the intellectual and commercial profits that were just around the corner.

2.2.2 Towards an effective therapy

Understandably, Banting was keen to test the effectiveness of his extract on diabetic humans. After all, Banting's quest, typical of a physician, was not knowledge for its own sake, but for a practical therapy. But doctors in charge of diabetic patients in the hospital wards of Toronto were disinclined to subject their patients to untried remedies—Banting and Best must have been all too well aware of the unreliability and occasional toxic side-effects of their extracts. Unbeknown to Macleod, they had risked administering an extract of the degenerate pancreas of a dog to a diabetic medical colleague of Banting's towards the end of 1921. The extract was administered by mouth; no beneficial result was discernible.

▷ Why is oral administration unlikely to be an effective route for insulin? As a clue, recall what sort of chemical insulin is.

▶ At the time it was not appreciated that insulin was a *protein* and would be broken down by the protein-splitting enzymes involved in digestion. *Injection* of the extract would have been a better option.

A second attempt, on a 14-year-old patient, Leonard Thompson, this time with Macleod's rather grudging approval, provided just sufficient cause for optimism to maintain Banting and Best's flagging spirits, even if others were unconvinced. A fall in blood sugar from 0.44 to 0.32 g% did follow intramuscular injection of extracts of degenerate pancreas, and the total amount of sugar excreted in the urine in a 24-hour period fell. Later Banting talked in exaggerated terms of this extract producing a 'marked reduction' in blood sugar (although in reality the fall was only about 25%) and of the resultant 'sugar-free urine'. But from a medical view there were serious adverse reactions; impurities in the extract caused an abscess to develop at the site of injection, which prompted the disappointing verdict that 'No clinical benefit was evidenced' and the general medical conclusion that Banting and Best's extract had been a failure.

It needed a chemist's skills to enable the production of a purer insulin preparation. These were provided by James Collip, who was researching at the University of Toronto whilst on sabbatical leave from his own university and who, at Banting's request, joined the team temporarily in late 1921. Collip has since been described as 'part chef, part brewer, part wizard' and less kindly, as 'part messer'. By imaginative and lengthy processes of trial and error, involving, for example, alterations in the timing and sequence of key steps, such as mixing, filtering and evaporating, he was able to effect a number of improvements in the extraction technique. Alcohol offered the best chance of success. The different proteins present in the pancreatic extract (of which one, insulin, was the desired target) were soluble in alcohol of different concentrations to varying degrees. Collip found that many of the contaminating proteins present precipitated out from solution at low alcohol concentrations, leaving the 'active ingredient', i.e. insulin, behind in solution. At a higher alcohol concentration, insulin itself precipitated out. Many of the salts and fats present could be eliminated by chemical tricks of the trade, leading to a powder that, though still contaminated, was far purer than any extract obtained hitherto.

This was only part of Collip's success; he had found fairly early on in his work that his extracts not only had the ability to reduce blood sugar levels in diabetic dogs, but they could also increase the glycogen content of their livers. So, here was convincing evidence that what he termed this 'mysterious something' had just the properties expected of the elusive hormone.

The news of Collip's success with the extraction of insulin was communicated to Banting and Best in a rather abrupt style, as the following extract from Banting's reminiscences of 1940 makes clear:

> *The worst blow fell one evening towards the end of January (1922). Collip had become less and less communicative and finally after a week's absence he came into our little room about five-thirty one evening. He stopped inside the door and said, 'Well fellows, I've got it.' I turned and said, 'Fine, congratulations. How did you do it?' Collip replied, 'I have decided not to tell you.'*

Collip then claimed Macleod's backing for his stance, which implied that a new and divisive alignment now alienated Banting and Best from their two colleagues. Banting seemed at this stage to resent Collip's presence; Collip, whose opinion of Banting was not high, felt, with considerable justification, that his chemical flair had rescued the research from the doldrums. Furthermore, Banting knew that Collip used *fresh* (i.e. non-degenerate) pancreatic tissue as the starting point. At this point he must have realized that the cumbersome and time-consuming ligation procedure to produce a degenerate pancreas was all in vain—a heart-breaking conclusion to all his painstaking surgical work of the previous year.

This brief episode indicates an all-pervasive air of paranoia and mistrust, fuelled by exhaustion and excitement, by Collip's unpredictable temperament and by Banting's anxiety that others were now undeservedly enjoying the success and credit that sprung from his initial inspiration. In true professorial tradition, Macleod tried to pacify an irate Banting and reconciliation was attempted in the form of a written agreement between the major warring parties, stressing the need for co-operation and consultation. This did little to raise Banting's spirits; an increasing sense of isolation and despair drove him (temporarily) to drink for consolation, finding a more indulgent use for the 95% alcohol that had formed a key part of Collip's extraction technique.

Bruised feelings apart, the more positive outcome of Collip's endeavours was a reasonably pure extract that could be used on diabetic patients. Early in 1922, Leonard Thompson's urinary sugar fell to 'almost nothing' and his blood sugar fell by about 80% following injections of Collip's extract. He reported 'feeling stronger'. This was the first of many glowingly favourable results that soon attracted interest and acclaim, from doctors, patients and from the increasingly excited world-at-large.

However, in the months immediately after this discovery, there were problems with both the therapeutic use and the commercial supply of insulin. There were con-siderable difficulties in scaling up the production of insulin from Collip's improvised laboratory procedures to a commercial undertaking able to meet the booming demands for the hormone. Protracted legal arguments surrounded the patenting of the discovery and the commercial licensing for manufacture. Establishing the most suitable source of insulin was problematic too; fortunately, as Banting and Best had discovered, insulins could work across species boundaries. Indeed, Banting temporarily favoured fish pancreas as the best source of insulin (the advantage is that in the fish pancreas, unlike that of mammals, the Islets are anatomically separate from the remaining pancreatic tissue, rather than dispersed within it). Prolonged trials and errors eventually pointed to the sizeable pancreases of the pig and the cow as the most convenient starting points for insulin extraction. Indeed, most of the insulin used routinely by diabetic patients thereafter came from these sources; that is, until the introduction of human insulin in the 1980s, in circumstances we describe in Chapter 3.

Seventy years on, it is difficult to recapture the sense of euphoria that the discovery of insulin engendered—diabetics who had faced certain death were given hope of

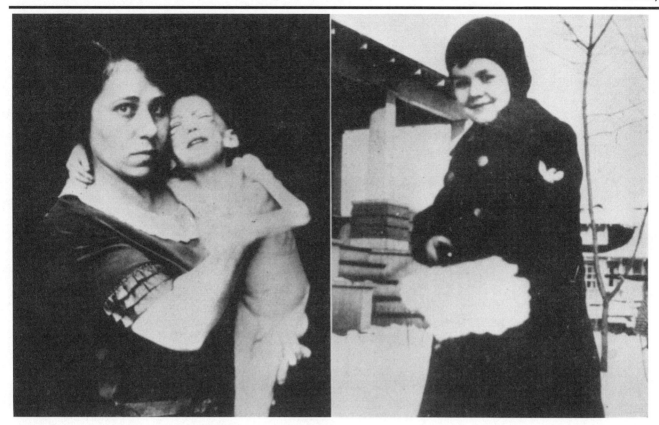

Figure 2.6 (left) Mother with her child in the 'terminal' stages of diabetes. (right) The same child shovelling snow 32 days after insulin treatment had begun.

restoration to a near-normal life. Insulin indeed produced a miraculous transformation, much more so than nowadays, simply because patients were initially in such an ill and undernourished state. Then, as now, eager journalists spread the word, glorifying brave patients and the miracles of modern medical science in equal measure, but for once there was little need for exaggeration. An 11-year-old girl was brought back to normal life following several hours of deep unconsciousness; days later she was playing happily; three months later she was back at school, with years of comparatively normal life ahead. Figure 2.6 provides visible evidence of the scale and speed of transformation. A similar case prompted a colleague of Banting to say: 'it still remains a wonder that this limpid liquid injected under the skin twice a day can metamorphose a frail baby, child, adult, or old man or woman to their nearly normal counterparts'.

Within two years of the discovery of insulin, when commercial production of insulin became better established, the lives of thousands of diabetic patients around the world were transformed. The resulting mood of public optimism imagined medical science relentlessly marching forward to conquer all other human ills.

2.2.3 The aftermath — an ignoble squabble

Despite, or more likely because of, the increasing chorus of approval and congratulation, the mood within the Toronto group remained discordant. Jealousies and recrimination were very much to the fore, and were now made more intense by concerns about where the credit for the discovery of insulin would be assigned. The atmosphere was made worse by a damning criticism of Banting and Best's work produced by English researchers towards the end of 1922.

▷   Identify one major error in Banting and Best's published work.

▶   Their adherence to the hypothesis that in a normal pancreas, the external secretion would destroy the internal secretion during the extraction process (see Activity 2.3e).

The absence of effective controls was also noted (e.g. see Activity 2.3c), together with the fact that many of the dogs that were used were in an abnormal condition. All in all, the thrilling discovery of insulin could not disguise 'wrongly conceived, wrongly conducted and wrongly interpreted experiments'. The implication was that Banting and Best had stumbled across insulin more by accident than by design. Macleod, who could not claim ignorance in defence, was implicated too, prompting the unkind comment from an envious contemporary that 'insulin could only have been discovered in a laboratory whose director was slightly stupid'.

Banting and Best's critics went further, asserting that the initial hypothesis should have been abandoned even before an experiment had been performed! Banting had been concerned mainly about the destructive effects of the protein-splitting enzyme trypsin in the external secretion. But he made no attempt to test experimentally whether such breakdown of the anti-diabetic factor in fact occurred during its extraction from the pancreas. Had he done so, a surprise would have been in store.

As early as 1921 it was known that trypsin is secreted from the pancreas in an *inactive* form (as trypsinogen) and it normally becomes effective only after passing along the pancreatic duct into the intestine; there it is activated by a factor produced by the cells lining the intestinal wall. The implication is that no active protein-splitting enzyme would be present in the extract of fresh pancreas, suggesting that the anti-diabetic factor would be intact. It was likely that Banting and Best were unaware of this—they were certainly not fully abreast of the literature. Perhaps they *did* know, but reasoned that *some* active trypsin (or some other agent) would be present in the pancreatic tissue after its removal from the animal, able to break down insulin—this wouldn't have been the first time that an 'established fact' from the scientific literature proved to be wrong. (However, no such detailed reasoning is evident in Banting's extensive laboratory notes from the period.) But if an active trypsin had been present, a key step in the extraction procedure followed by Banting and Best would have rendered any such enzyme inactive. For, as is usual practice, the extract was kept *chilled* during its preparation, at temperatures sufficiently low to prevent enzymes such as trypsin breaking down insulin. The implication of all this is that the use of the degenerate pancreas as a starting point—Banting's 'great idea'—was inappropriate and unnecessary. Remember that Collip (and Banting and Best themselves, unknowingly) had shown that extracts of *fresh* pancreas were effective.

With good intentions, Macleod defended his less worldly-wise junior colleagues against such criticism, claiming that their initial experiments had been 'the first essential step' in the right direction. This proper sentiment enraged an already over-reactive Banting, now obsessed with a concern to acquire the lion's share of the credit for the discovery of insulin. His dislike for Macleod was particularly intense and destructive, feelings that mellowed little with the passage of time. Banting subsequently wrote:

> *Macleod ... was never to be trusted. He was the most selfish man I have ever known. He was grasping, selfish, deceptive, self-seeking and empty of truth, yet he was clever as a speaker and writer. He was unscrupulous and would steal an idea or credit for any work from any possible source.*

This indictment is more revealing of Banting's character than of Macleod's; the clear consensus from those who knew Macleod and judged him more dispassionately was of a decent, well-intentioned man, an able but not inspired worker who bravely and persistently sought to manage a volatile situation, where jealousy, insecurity and greed sat alongside the painful process of unravelling scientific truth.

With an atypically speedy judgement, recognizing the importance of this major breakthrough in the control of disease, the Nobel Committee decided to award the 1923 prize in Physiology or Medicine to the discoverers of insulin. But which of them could be said to have *discovered* insulin, and when? If the crucial stage was establishing the existence of a 'something' from the pancreas that had anti-diabetic qualities, then others (such as Paulesco) could claim priority (as indeed they did after the Committee's announcement). Better therefore to recognize the moment of discovery as the first successful and safe use of an extract on a human, to (temporarily) relieve diabetic symptoms.

▷   Could Banting and Best *alone* claim the discovery on these grounds?

▸   No, their own extracts provided no convincing evidence of an anti-diabetic factor. Their first (administered by mouth) had had no effect; their second (on Leonard Thompson) did reduce diabetic symptoms (very modestly) but impurities caused an abscess.

Activity 2.4

(a) In your view, who in the Toronto group should have got the credit for the discovery of insulin? State your views in a couple of sentences.

Then, referring where necessary to the preceding text, answer (b) and (c), in each case in less than 80 words.

(b) In what respect was Macleod's input essential to the discovery of insulin?

(c) Most modern observers believe that Collip deserved a share of the credit. What is the justification for this?

Detailed investigation of the circumstances, leaning heavily on soundings taken from 'the great and the good', eventually led the Nobel Committee to announce that the 1923 prize was to be shared equally between Banting and Macleod. Any momentary delight that Banting may have displayed was overwhelmed by anger concerning Macleod's inclusion and Best's omission. Contemporary accounts tell of Banting threatening to turn down the prize, interspersed with much 'helling and damning'; to his credit, he chose a more positive course of action, electing to share the glory of science's greatest honour by splitting his portion of the prize money with Best.

Macleod responded by offering to share half of his prize money with Collip, thereby ensuring that all the key players in the saga received due credit. (The failure to officially recognize Collip's contribution is seen by many as an unfortunate oversight by the Nobel Committee; see Activity 2.4.) Macleod's statement to the press emphasized the importance of 'team work' and the key role of Collip. He saw the discovery as a 'multi-step process', judging correctly that Banting and Best could not have brought their ideas to a successful conclusion without advice and guidance. Whether Macleod appreciated his own faults in failing to recognize the flaws in the experiments is uncertain, but he certainly saw his own role as crucial. When prompted by the press to say more about his own work in the discovery, he replied with unconvincing modesty that he was 'only the impresario—the managing director'.

Summary of Chapter 2

1 Diabetes mellitus, if untreated, is a life-threatening disease, resulting from the body's inability to utilize glucose effectively. Prior to the discovery of insulin in Ontario in 1922, there was no effective therapy for the disease.

2 Prior to 1922, it was thought that diabetes was attributable to a malfunction of the pancreas and in particular of the Islets of Langerhans, which appeared normally to produce an internal secretion that had anti-diabetic properties.

3 Prior to the work of Banting and Best, extracts of healthy pancreas were found to have uncertain and inconsistent effects on diabetic animals and humans.

4 Banting was inspired to work on diabetes because of his initial (erroneous) supposition that in the extraction process, the digestive enzymes in the external secretion of the pancreas would destroy the anti-diabetic hormone from the Islets. This concern prompted his use of 'degenerate' pancreas, where the pancreatic duct had previously been ligated.

5 Banting and Best's experiments to identify the proposed hormone insulin were faulty in conception and execution. In particular, a potent anti-diabetic extract could be obtained from fresh pancreas (containing external secretion) and experiments were often conducted without the effective controls that other workers, notably Macleod, suggested.

6 Collip was responsible for a major improvement in the extraction technique, using fresh pancreas, which resulted in a safe and effective extract that consistently relieved diabetic symptoms in humans. At this point, insulin can be said to have been 'discovered', bringing to fruition a line of investigation initiated by Banting and Best's early experiments.

7 Administration of insulin to diabetics produced a 'miraculous' transformation, offering an opportunity for a near-normal life to those who otherwise were certain to die prematurely.

8 The discovery of insulin did not arise from carefully designed and controlled experiments and the strict application of scientific methodology; chance observations, erroneous assumptions, exaggerated conclusions and luck all played a part. An atmosphere of increasing bitterness and rivalry soured the relationships between the Toronto co-workers.

9 Banting and Macleod shared the 1923 Nobel prize for Physiology or Medicine. Banting shared his part of the prize with Best and was resentful of Macleod's recognition. Macleod shared his with Collip, whose key role in the extraction of insulin should probably have been recognized by the Nobel Committee.

Question 2.1 Which one of the following statements about the action of insulin is correct?

(a) It increases the uptake of glucose by liver and muscle cells.

(b) It is released by the enzyme-producing cells of the pancreas.

(c) It is released from the Islet cells when glucose levels start to fall.

(d) Once present in the bloodstream, insulin immediately has a prolonged and substantial effect over 10–12 hours in reducing blood glucose.

Question 2.2 Place the following events in the correct chronological sequence.

(a) First successful use of insulin therapeutically.

(b) Identification of the Islets of Langerhans.

(c) Internal secretion named insulin.

(d) Islets identified as the likely site of production of internal secretion.

(e) Knowledge of high sugar content in urine of diabetics.

(f) Extracts of degenerate pancreas injected into diabetics.

Question 2.3 Which one of the following most accurately describes the purpose served by Banting and Best's initial ligation experiments?

(a) They showed that the internal secretion could be extracted only after the enzyme-secreting portion of the pancreas had degenerated.

(b) They showed conclusively that the fall in blood sugar levels following injection of the pancreatic extract was due to the insulin it contained.

(c) They showed that the internal secretion contained very few other contaminating chemicals besides insulin.

(d) They put them 'on the right track', convincing them that the internal secretion did contain the anti-diabetic factor, and that this was available for extraction.

3 Development

As we saw in Chapter 2, the discovery of insulin brought about a new spirit of optimism, with an expectation that other killer diseases would soon be conquered. Informed medical opinion contributed to the euphoric atmosphere by overstating insulin's powers, often combined with exaggerated pronouncements of a 'new epoch in medicine'.

One of the few discordant voices emanated from a well-orchestrated anti-vivisectionist campaign, both in Britain and in Canada, which attempted to deny insulin's effectiveness, out of an ingrained hostility to therapy derived from animal experimentation. It was not difficult for such campaigners to find examples of discontented diabetic patients, especially since usable insulin was at first in short supply; however, understandably, it was next to impossible to find diabetics with sufficiently strong ethical reservations about animal experimentation to forego treatment. But in two respects the claims of the anti-vivisectionists were right: insulin was certainly not a *cure* for diabetes, neither was its use in the treatment of the disease entirely trouble-free.

It was soon apparent that the problem of diabetes had not gone away with the discovery of insulin. Major problems remained, including establishing how much insulin should be used by diabetic patients and what sort of special diet, if any, should be adopted. Furthermore, long-term complications of the disease such as kidney damage and circulatory problems became apparent. So the euphoria was gradually replaced by the realization that the disease was much more complex than had previously been thought. As Michael Bliss has pointed out, the events in Toronto marked not the end of the study of how to treat diabetes but only its beginning.

Given the limits of time and space, we can include here only a few of the major advances that have been made in more recent years. What will become clear is that the treatment of diabetes has been revolutionized over the past 70 years and that improvements have been brought about both by technical advances and by a greatly increased understanding of the scientific basis of the disease. But as you will see, new knowledge has also raised new questions and dilemmas for doctors and diabetic patients alike.

3.1 Changes of attitude and increased understanding

At the beginning of the 20th century, there was a widespread medical belief that the less diabetic patients ate, the longer they would survive. Although insulin soon became a major tool in the treatment of diabetes in the years following Banting and Best's work, the medical profession's adherence to strict dietary control lingered on. Today's elderly diabetic patients can still recall the early days of stringent diets, for example of cabbage water and brussel sprouts, along with painful injections. The strict instruction of the day was that children with diabetes should avoid exercise. With time, dietary restrictions eased. Today, dietary control is still a key part of diabetes therapy but there is less emphasis on a rigid 'diabetic diet', which in earlier times had required patients to adhere religiously to a few staple foods and fixed meal times. Special 'diabetic' products which at one time were pre-eminent in the control of diabetes (see Figure 3.1) are now considered inappropriate by both the medical profession and the British Diabetic Association. (In fact they both advise a diet very similar to the usual recommended healthy diet, i.e. low in fat and sugar and high in fibre.)

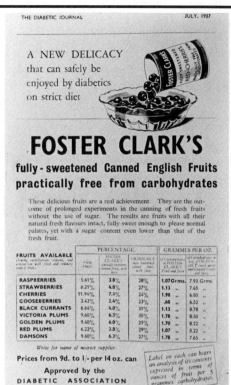

Figure 3.1 These advertisements, both from 1937 issues of *The Diabetic Journal*, show the former emphasis on special sugar-free products in the strict diets of diabetic patients.

The factors that prompted changes in attitude and practice in the UK had little to do with medicine. The hardships of the Second World War meant that the established diabetic diets and 'special' products were impractical. Diabetic individuals were obliged to take greater personal responsibility for managing their disease, adapting the normal wartime diet to their own special needs. Moreover, many sufferers excelled at wartime jobs hitherto classed as 'unsuitable for diabetics'—for example, in the emergency services. The post-war establishment of the National Health Service and the increased support from newly-founded specialized clinics provided more effective medical care. Diabetic patients were thus increasingly able to shake off the 'invalid' label that they had carried for so long and look forward to a fuller life-style and better health.

3.1.1 The two types of diabetes mellitus

Besides these important social changes, there have been major advances in recent years in our understanding of the biological basis of the disease. In particular, it is now well established that there are at least two types of diabetes mellitus, which differ in terms of both underlying cause and outward symptoms. The more dangerous, but less common, affects mainly juveniles, and it develops because of an inability to manufacture and release insulin; it is therefore called (especially in the USA) **insulin-dependent diabetes mellitus, IDDM**, or more commonly in European medical circles, **type 1 diabetes**. It is also sometimes referred to as juvenile-onset diabetes. Without insulin, those who suffer from type 1 diabetes will eventually die, as Banting and Best's young patients so tragically demonstrated.

It is now known that type 1 diabetes arises, in the first instance, because of a malfunction of the cells of the human body which are normally concerned with defence against disease; in particular, the specialized white blood cells that produce **antibodies** which can destroy foreign, invading materials. Some time well before the outward manifestation of the symptoms of diabetes, particular antibodies (and cells of the immune system) act against some of the body's *own* cells, particularly those of the Islets of Langerhans. Type 1 diabetes is therefore one of a range of so-called **auto-immune diseases** (rheumatoid arthritis is another); some sort of environmental trigger is thought to initiate this 'self-destruction'—possibly a commonplace viral infection or a dietary factor. The most compelling recent evidence on the cause of type 1 diabetes, which we explore in Activity 3.1, implicates *both* viral infection *and* diet.

Activity 3.1 *You should spend up to 20 minutes on this activity.*

Use each of the following observations (1–6) to construct, in not more than about 100 words, a *hypothesis* that *might* explain how type 1 diabetes arises. Identify the observations that support each of the points you make.

1 Cow's milk contains a large protein called bovine serum albumin (BSA), which, in bottle-fed infants, can sometimes pass from the baby's intestine into its blood.

2 Populations who traditionally avoid cow's milk for infant feeding have a very low incidence of type 1 diabetes, for example Western Samoans. Western Samoans brought up in New Zealand, where they are more inclined to adopt bottle-feeding, have a higher incidence of type 1 diabetes.

3 The insulin-producing Islet cells of the pancreas normally have a protein (called p69) on their outer membrane; for reasons that are unknown, in infants the amount of p69 protein on these cells increases substantially with viral infection.

4 Infants who are bottle-fed on cow's milk can produce antibodies to one portion of the BSA protein in their blood; children recently diagnosed as diabetic have about seven times the normal quantity of anti-BSA antibodies in their blood.

5 One portion of the BSA molecule is chemically very similar to the p69 protein; anti-BSA antibodies present in young diabetic patients destroy both BSA and p69 protein.

6 When p69 is present in large amounts on the surface of insulin-producing cells and is attacked by anti-BSA antibodies, the cells die.

It is very important that you appreciate that Activity 3.1 focused on a single, plausible explanation of the cause of type 1 diabetes, consistent with the evidence presented here. However, supporting evidence exists for a whole range of specific hypotheses about the environmental trigger that initiates Islet cell malfunction; only time will tell if this particular hypothesis proves accurate. Even if it turns out to be substantially correct, details are likely to change. For example, it may not be the antibodies themselves that knock out p69 directly (see observation 6 above), but perhaps some other component of the immune system.

Why particular infants are over-reactive to BSA in the first few months of life is, as yet, unknown. What is perplexing is that the incidence of the disease is changing, and here too the reasons are unclear.

Activity 3.2

Read Extract 3.1. Summarize three significant pieces of information about the incidence of childhood (i.e. type 1) diabetes that have not already been mentioned.

Extract 3.1   From *The Guardian*, 22 February 1991.

Public health concern voiced as researchers find one child under five diagnosed every day

Cases of child diabetes double

Chris Mihill
Medical Correspondent

THE number of cases of childhood diabetes has nearly doubled over the past 15 years, raising a considerable public health concern, researchers say today.

In 1974 a survey found that the annual rate at which insulin-dependent diabetes was diagnosed in children under the age of 15 was 7.7 per 100 000 of the population. A new survey has found the rate is now 13.5 per 100 000.

The researchers, Alison Metcalfe and Professor David Baum, from the Royal Hospital for Sick Children, Bristol, collected all cases diagnosed during 1988. They say the increase is not due to more cases being looked for, but represents a real rise.

The growth is possibly caused by environmental factors, or the illness developing at an earlier age in susceptible children, they suggest.

The researchers found a total of 1 600 children throughout the United Kingdom and the Irish Republic with diabetes, with a quarter of these being under five years old. In the earlier survey 19 per cent were under five. Diabetes researchers have been puzzled for some time by the finding that the further north of the Equator a country lies, the higher the incidence of diabetes.

The Bristol study confirms this, with Scotland having 19.8 cases per 100 000. It also found regional variations: Ireland had a lower rate than expected, 6.8 cases per 100 000, as did two London regions. East Anglia, Wessex, and the Northern region had higher than expected rates.

The Bristol doctors, publishing their findings in the British Medical Journal, state: 'On average, at least one child under the age of five years had diabetes diagnosed each day during 1988'.

They add: 'If diabetes is becoming more common in this age group, possibly by developing earlier in susceptible children, this would be a matter of considerable public health concern'.

The researchers point out that the British Isles rate lies midway between the country with the highest incidence, Finland (28.6 cases per 100 000), and the lowest, Japan (1.7 cases per 100 000).

Last night Professor Baum said: 'One environmental variable that is being particularly carefully looked at is diet'.

The British Diabetic Association said that it had found a similar increase.

The cause of the illness was not understood, the association said. It was worrying that more young children seemed to be developing the condition. Apart from the pain and inconvenience of daily insulin injections, there was evidence that the earlier the condition occurred, the more chance there was of complications such as blindness or kidney disease developing.

The second, more common form of the disease is sometimes termed maturity-onset diabetes, a term that gives a clue to those who are susceptible; for reasons that will soon become clear, it is more properly termed **non-insulin-dependent diabetes mellitus (NIDDM)** or **type 2 diabetes**. It is a disease of later life, and many type 2 diabetes patients are overweight. In the UK, probably about half a million adults have type 2 diabetes, representing about 2% of people over 40 years of age. The symptoms of the disease are somewhat like those of type 1 diabetes, though less severe, and are again the consequence of hyperglycaemia, i.e. thirst and copious urine production. However, a dramatic loss of weight is unlikely. What is also different here is that insulin levels in the blood are not usually abnormally low—indeed they can sometimes be exceptionally *high*. The insulin-producing cells are not significantly reduced in number at the onset of the disease but the rate and pattern of insulin secretion is often abnormal. Such diabetic patients are therefore usually not treated routinely with insulin injections. Restriction of diet is normally the first line of attack, sometimes followed by oral administration of drugs that increase insulin secretion (by stimulating the insulin-secreting cells directly) and therefore reduce blood glucose levels. Often, as the disease progresses, the release of large amounts of insulin can result in physiological 'exhaustion' of the pancreas; so type 2 patients may eventually require regular administration of insulin.

The reasons for the onset of type 2 diabetes are unknown—often there is reduced sensitivity of the target cells of the body to insulin. This results in limited uptake of blood glucose by the muscles and the liver, and hence leads to hyperglycaemia. It seems that the receptors are still able to bind insulin but that this binding no longer initiates an effective response of the cell to the hormone—thus cells cannot increase their uptake of glucose, even if large amounts of insulin are present. This condition is known as **insulin resistance**; it is usually combined with a variable degree of impairment of insulin secretion from the Islet cells.

There is some evidence that the type 2 diabetes may result from the combined effects of poor nutrition in early life and an over-rich diet as a mature adult. It seems that the numbers of insulin-producing cells in the pancreas, and their functioning, are determined at the foetal stage; these cells undergo few divisions after birth. If the nutrition of the foetus is poor (perhaps because of poor maternal diet) there may be a relatively small number of insulin-producing cells, each perhaps 'programmed' for such a deficient diet. With the richer diet of later life, typical of overweight individuals, such 'lean-tuned' cells may not be able to rise to the extra metabolic demands. This is unlikely to be the full explanation for the onset of type 2 diabetes—genetic factors, perhaps together with additional hormonal and environmental influences, play a part in a complex set of interactions. But it does now seem that for both type 1 and type 2 diabetes, nutrition very early in life could play a part in the onset of the disease.

The relative ease of early treatment, together with the fact that many individuals who have type 2 diabetes do not display any symptoms (indeed many sufferers will remain undiagnosed) initially prompted use of the term 'mild' to describe this type of diabetes. This term is now, understandably, out of favour because it fails to acknowledge the severe complications that can sometimes arise, just as with type 1 diabetes—for example kidney malfunction and blindness, of which we shall say more later on.*

3.1.2 How blood glucose levels are controlled

Unknown to Banting and Best, it is now apparent that insulin is only *one* of an array of pancreatic hormones that help control blood glucose levels. **Glucagon** is another hormone produced within the Islets of Langerhans, but by a different population of cells than those secreting insulin.

Activity 3.3

What can you deduce about the function and production of glucagon from each of the following observations? (*Note*: Be careful to distinguish here between *glycogen* and *glucagon*.)

(a) When glucagon is added to slices of liver *in vitro*, it promotes the breakdown of glycogen stored within the liver cells, and glucose is released into the surrounding medium.

(b) When a non-diabetic individual is made hypoglycaemic (e.g. by oral administration of an appropriate drug), glucagon release from the pancreas is triggered; glucagon release falls off when blood glucose levels are raised.

(c) Low levels of insulin in the blood (or prolonged starvation or prolonged exercise) can trigger glucagon release, which results in an elevation of blood glucose levels.

---

* In the remainder of this text the term diabetes is used to encompass both conditions, except where it is important to distinguish between type 1 and type 2 diabetes mellitus.

Your answers to Activity 3.3 should imply that insulin and glucagon act *antagonistically*, i.e. in opposite directions: glucagon promotes glycogen breakdown and raises blood glucose levels; insulin promotes glycogen synthesis and lowers blood glucose levels. Furthermore, while *low* levels of glucose stimulate glucagon release (Activity 3.3b), insulin release is triggered by *raised* levels of blood glucose. As Activity 3.3c implied, the level of one hormone can influence the rate of release of its antagonist, in this case, a low level of insulin stimulates glucagon release. (Glucagon levels can influence insulin secretion but in a complex way that we need not consider.) This is a pattern reminiscent of many control processes in the human body where the 'steady state' is maintained by a delicate balance between two (or more) hormones with opposite effects.

In fact, it is now well established that there are *four* different types of hormone-producing cells in the pancreatic Islets, three of which are implicated in glucose regulation. Insulin is produced by so-called B (or beta, β) cells (see Figure 2.1b and Plates 2.1b and c); A (or alpha, α) cells produce glucagon. A third hormone (called *somatostatin*), again produced by discrete groups of Islet cells, regulates the fine tuning of the release of the other two hormones, probably on a minute-by-minute basis. Other hormones, produced in tissues other than the pancreas, also exert an effect on blood glucose levels, notably *adrenalin*.

So the control of blood glucose is very complex and, not surprisingly, our understanding of the process is incomplete. Though many hormones are involved, treating diabetes with an appropriate 'cocktail' is impractical—insulin exerts the dominant influence and is still today the focus for treatment. Nowadays, it is administered with the aim of keeping blood glucose levels as close to normal as possible, i.e. the aim is to achieve **tight control**. Given the complexity of the control processes involved—which we have only glimpsed at here—and the number of different processes that are pulling glucose out of or pushing it into the bloodstream, this is a far from easy undertaking. The amount of insulin injected, and at what times, are crucial parameters, but the precise effects of injection depend upon a host of factors, including exercise, diet and general state of health. It has also become apparent that diabetes involves far more than a disturbance of carbohydrate metabolism—it has knock-on effects on metabolism in general, in ways not readily controlled by insulin injection. For all these reasons, insulin is one of the most difficult drugs to use to best effect.

A major problem, especially in type 1 diabetes, is the risk of hypoglycaemia from injecting too much insulin, or taking too much exercise or too little food, or a combination of these factors.

▷ From Figure 2.2, what is the approximate blood glucose threshold for the onset of hypoglycaemia?

▶ About $3\,\text{mmol}\,\text{l}^{-1}$ blood glucose, at which point the majority of diabetic patients sense the onset of a hypoglycaemic episode—a 'hypo'.

So those who are diabetic have to be wary of injecting too large a dose of insulin, which will stimulate glucose uptake too vigorously, possibly causing a 'hypo'. (We saw the risks of such an effect in Figure 2.2, with injection A.) Some of the initial, mild symptoms of hypoglycaemia were mentioned in Section 2.1—drowsiness, headache, nausea. A full hypoglycaemic episode is distressing; behaviour becomes increasingly bizarre and unpredictable, leading if unchecked to convulsions and loss of consciousness, due to the reduction of glucose supply to the brain. Nearly all diabetic patients learn to recognize the particular 'warning signs' and take remedial action, i.e. they have **hypoglycaemic awareness**.

▷   What two remedies would you suggest for hypoglycaemia? Suggest one involving tablets and another involving the administration of a hormone.

▶   Glucose tablets would be a quick and effective remedy. If this is ineffective, or if the patient is already unconscious, the injection of glucagon (or adrenalin) will help raise glucose levels by promoting the breakdown of glycogen, particularly in the liver.

Up until the mid-1970s, the general consensus in the medical profession was that it was next to impossible to ensure that any insulin injection regime could maintain blood glucose levels in type 1 diabetes patients at normal values for long periods. The main fear was that successive insulin injections would increase the risks of hypoglycaemia, with all the attendant dangers. Diabetic patients were therefore commonly hyperglycaemic, as Figure 2.2 implied. As we have said, in recent years attitudes have changed, and there is now an increased emphasis on 'tighter' control of blood glucose. The reasons for this change of approach are worth considering in some detail.

First, evidence accumulated throughout the 1970s of the medical advantages of tight control. Because diabetics were living longer on insulin, secondary complications were becoming better understood. Patients with long-standing type 1 diabetes were proving 25 times more prone to blindness than the general population and 17 times more likely to suffer from kidney disease. It also became apparent that the nerve damage sometimes associated with long-established diabetes could lead to loss of sensation in the limb extremities. As we have mentioned, type 2 diabetes patients also developed such complications. Most of these effects were thought to derive from the long-term toxic influence of raised blood glucose levels, which suggested that avoidance of hyperglycaemia should be a priority.

Secondly, in the late 1970s techniques became available to enable patients to measure routinely their *own* blood glucose levels, i.e. to do self-monitoring. Such techniques employ test strips impregnated with a substance (the reagent) that reacts with glucose, undergoing a colour change that is dependent on the amount of glucose present. A drop of blood is applied to the reagent test strip, the blood sample is blotted and the developed colour is checked by eye against a standard chart (see Plate 3.1).

There have recently been major advances in self-monitoring techniques, as the next section illustrates, but the simple early devices brought an unexpected benefit; they enabled both doctors and patients to see for the first time just how bad the control of blood glucose levels could sometimes be—and provided both the data and the means needed to point the way to tighter control! For the first time, maintenance of normal blood glucose levels on an hour-by-hour basis became a realizable goal, with the patient having a prominent role in the decision-making.

3.2 New technology for old

Another factor that contributed to a change of attitude was the development, towards the end of the 1970s, of mechanical devices that could achieve tight control of blood glucose for diabetics, with largely beneficial results for the patient.

Figure 3.2 shows one such commercially produced pump that can be programmed by the patient to deliver set amounts of insulin at variable intervals. The reservoir of insulin is contained within the main body of the pump, which is normally fixed loosely to the side of the body. Leading from it is a fine plastic tube (or cannula), ending in a fine metal needle. The point of this needle is inserted by the patient

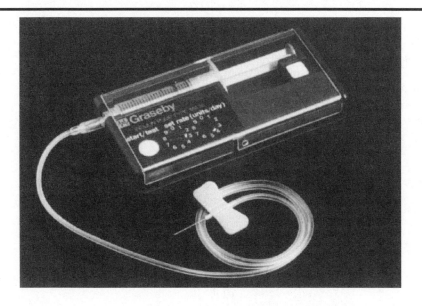

Figure 3.2 An insulin infusion pump used for CSII. This device is about $12\,cm \times 6\,cm \times 2.5\,cm$, i.e. similar in size to a pocket calculator.

beneath the skin (i.e. subcutaneously) and kept in position with the help of the 'butterfly' wings. Every couple of days, the insertion point is changed, to avoid damage to the skin or infection. The technique is called **continuous subcutaneous insulin infusion**, or **CSII**.

Tight control with CSII is certainly achievable in practice (see Figure 3.3), but of overriding importance is the acceptability of the technique to patients. At its present stage of development, the apparatus is moderately obtrusive and demands a high level of medical and technical support. CSII pumps have therefore yet to make an impact on the routine treatment of diabetes. Even with future refinements they may be suitable for only a small minority of type 1 diabetic patients.

More convenient would be a pump that could be implanted in the body for considerable periods of time. Up to now, probably fewer than 1 000 patients world-wide

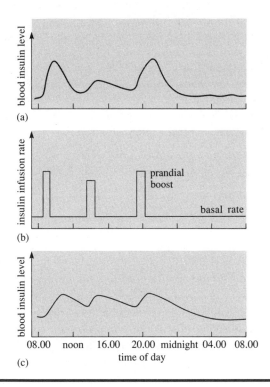

Figure 3.3 How normal insulin control is simulated by CSII. (a) shows the changing level of insulin in the blood of a healthy subject, over a 24-hour period—the pattern is similar to that in Figure 2.3. This is the true 'physiological' picture which techniques such as CSII try to emulate. (b) shows the rate at which insulin is automatically despatched from the pump into the tissues beneath the skin—the so-called infusion rate. Note that for most of the time, delivery is at a low or basal rate, simulating the low rate of insulin release in the fasting periods, i.e. the time between meals, in (a). Just before meals, the simple press of a button triggers a mealtime (i.e. prandial) boost, which, added to the basal release, produces peaks of insulin in the blood (c) that resemble the normal pattern in (a). This is largely because there is a time lag between insulin leaving the tip of the needle and being distributed through the bloodstream; this helps to smooth out the otherwise sharp rises.

have received such an **implanted insulin pump**, which is still at the experimental stage; however, because of the potential application of the device for delivery of a wide variety of drugs, research and development in this field is intense. Some such pumps can be programmed, using a remotely-controlled patient-operated radio-frequency programmer (see Figure 3.4), to deliver variable amounts of insulin. The technology required is complex, and the required standards of reliability are very high. Consequently, this type of implanted pump is very costly—at least £7 000 (1993 prices).

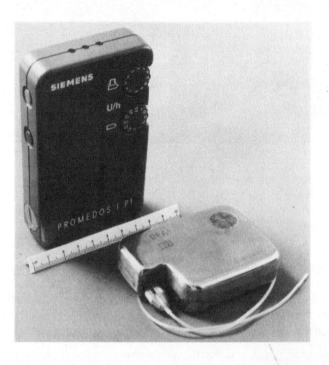

Figure 3.4 An implanted insulin pump. The implantable infusion unit is to the front, with the remote-control programming unit behind. Pumps are usually implanted close to the wall of the abdomen or near the shoulder blades. An insulin reservoir can be re-filled periodically by injection through the skin with a hypodermic needle. It is hoped that pumps such as these will be of special use to those patients for whom conventional insulin therapy or CSII has not resulted in satisfactory control of blood glucose.

As if refinement of pump technology is not problem enough, there are also biological complications. Being foreign bodies, even 'inert' materials, such as plastic, evoke a response from the body. Tissue will eventually grow in and around the fine tube that leads from the infusion unit (usually conveying insulin into a major vein) which will eventually become blocked, sometimes as soon as 18 months after implantation. Research into such **biocompatibility** problems is very active and there seems every reason to believe that this complication will be resolved, at least to the point where the interval between replacement of pump components will be greatly extended. At present, the advantages of such a pump are yet to be clearly proven, given its cost, and the surgical and biological complications involved.

The ultimate technological goal is a closed-loop system, rather than the pumps mentioned above, which are open-loop systems, because they lack any feedback capacity.

▷   Can you identify the key feature of a closed-loop system?

▶   As you can appreciate from Section 2.1, a 'sensing' device that will monitor blood glucose levels is required. Via feedback control, this will trigger the release of an appropriate measure of insulin to restore normal levels of glucose.

Of course there are formidable technical demands in constructing what is in effect an 'artificial pancreas', to duplicate what the human organ can normally undertake with consumate ease! It is perhaps fitting that major advances in this direction have been made by a research group in Toronto, Canada, which have led to the commercial

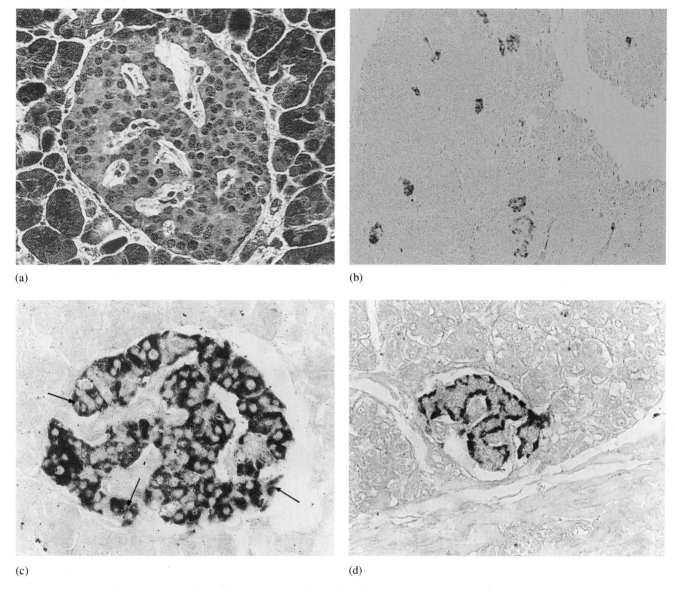

(a)

(b)

(c)

(d)

Plate 2.1 (a) A microscopic section of normal pancreas showing a single hormone-producing cell group surrounded by enzyme-producing cells (approximate magnification × 300). The stains used (haematoxylin and eosin) show up a wide variety of cell components. (b) is the result of a staining technique specific for insulin, showing a number of dark brown 'islands' scattered amongst the paler enzyme-producing cells; during processing, the tissue has become torn, see top right of section (approximate magnification × 20). (c) shows a single hormone-producing cell group from a normal pancreas where insulin in the cytoplasm is stained brown; the smaller amount of red staining (see arrows) shows the location of other hormones produced by the cell group (approximate magnification × 300). (d) is a comparable cell group from the pancreas of one type of diabetic patient — brown-stained cells are absent, leaving only red staining (approximate magnification × 300).

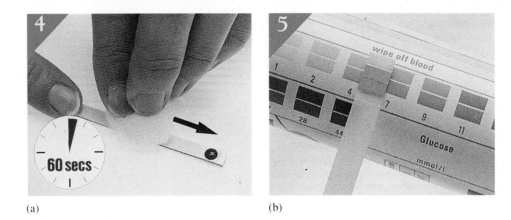

(a)   (b)

Plate 3.1   Self-monitoring test strips for blood glucose levels. (a) A drop of blood is applied to the strip and after 60 seconds, excess blood is wiped away. (b) After another wait of exactly 60 seconds, the colour that develops on the strip is compared to the standard colour blocks on the side of the container. These small test strips can measure glucose levels in the range 1–44 mmol l⁻¹. (The numbers in the top left-hand corner of each photo denote steps in the test procedure recommended by the manufacturer.)

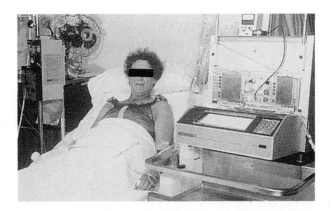

Plate 3.2   The Biostator artificial pancreas in use. Blood from a (superficial) vein is sampled continuously, and a conventional, externally-placed glucose analyser measures average glucose levels over 1 minute. These data feed into the computer, which can be pre-programmed with information on the patient's previous glucose record and responsiveness. The computer then triggers a delivery of glucose or of insulin back into the circulatory system. Excellent control of blood glucose has been achieved for a few patients continuously over several days, even under physiologically stressful conditions for the patient, for example during childbirth. The implantation of a catheter into a vein poses a small risk of thrombosis (i.e. formation of blood clots) and of infection. There are also some longer-term biocompatibility problems.

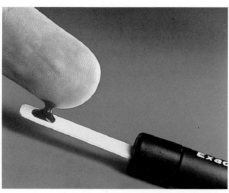
(a)

(b)

(c)

Plate 3.3 The ExacTech blood glucose sensor is available as (a) a pen meter or (b) a larger unit with a more sizeable display window, of particular use to diabetics with visual problems. The pen is only about 13 cm long. The electrodes are disposable and are unwrapped from their foil covering before insertion (c). Test solutions of known glucose concentrations are used to check accuracy; re-calibration of the meter is not usually required until after 50 electrode uses.

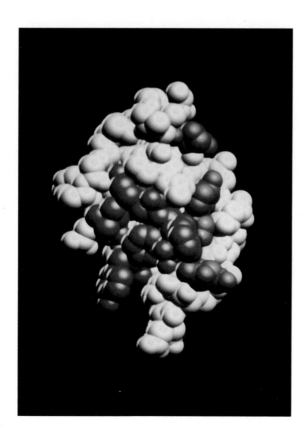

Plate 3.4 This is a 'receptor's-eye' view of insulin. It is a 'space-filling' model, showing in a highly-stylized way, the individual atoms that make up this two-chain protein molecule. There are five amino acids shown in red; these are on the B chain. They are known to be involved in the formation of insulin dimers and it is likely that they also function in receptor binding. The amino acids coloured blue are some of the A chain sites that are thought to be involved in receptor binding. Here they are partially covered by amino acids at one end of the B chain. These B chain amino acids may move away in the conformational change that accompanies binding, thereby exposing the key A chain amino acids underneath. As many as 18 amino acids in all may be involved in receptor binding.

production of the Biostator (shown in Plate 3.2). Its essential feature is that periodic blood glucose measurements are automatically used to determine the amount of insulin to be administered to the patient. The technical ingenuity is impressive but cannot disguise the drawbacks of cost, size and complexity. A long-term goal would be to miniaturize and implant such apparatus, but whether such a 'high-tech' solution to diabetes could or should ever become a routine form of treatment is an open question.

What might a miniaturized artificial pancreas of the future look like? The delivery part of such an artificial system might be similar in principle to that of the implanted pump shown in Figure 3.4, but linked to some kind of **glucose sensor**, which would continuously monitor blood glucose levels. A glucose sensor is a specialized type of **biosensor**. Biosensors are new devices that already have numerous applications in medicine; Figure 3.5 is a general explanation of how they function.

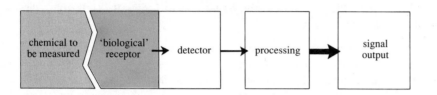

Figure 3.5 The mode of action of biosensors. The 'biological' receptor is shown in pink and can be a particular enzyme, antibody, cell, tissue or bacterium that will react specifically with the particular chemical being 'sensed' (i.e. measured); for example, a small molecule in the blood or a specific protein. The reaction leads to an instantaneous change (for example, the generation of an electric current, or of a pulse of heat or of light) which is picked up by a detector, which could be an electrode, a thermistor or a photodetector. Subsequent processing includes storage and amplification of the signal.

Glucose sensors have already been developed, mostly in the form of **enzyme electrodes**. The enzyme used for glucose sensing, glucose oxidase, is immobilized, for example within a thin membrane, very close to an electrode (see Figure 3.6). Glucose oxidase catalyses the following reaction:

$$\text{glucose} + O_2 \xrightarrow{\text{glucose oxidase}} \text{gluconic acid} + H_2O_2 \tag{3.1}$$

The amount of glucose present can be conveniently measured by detecting changes in the generation of hydrogen peroxide, H_2O_2, as indicated in Equation 3.1. The current flow from the positively charged platinum electrode shown in Figure 3.6 will be a measure of H_2O_2 production because of the following reaction:

$$H_2O_2 \longrightarrow O_2 + 2H^+ + 2e^- \tag{3.2}$$

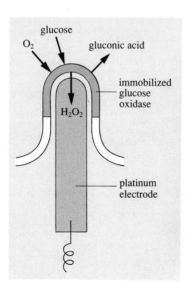

Figure 3.6 One type of enzyme electrode used for glucose sensing. This enzyme electrode monitors glucose concentration by detecting changes in the production of hydrogen peroxide (H_2O_2) in the glucose oxidase reaction (Equation 3.1). Equation 3.2 shows the reaction that occurs at the positively charged platinum electrode: each molecule of H_2O_2 breaks down producing two electrons. Thus the amount of current flow is a measure of the quantity of H_2O_2 and thus of the concentration of glucose (Equation 3.1).

▷   What alternative methods (i.e. other than that involving the decomposition of the H_2O_2 product) could monitor the rate of the reaction shown in Equation 3.1?

▶   The measurement of changes in the consumption of oxygen (using an oxygen electrode) or in the rate of production of gluconic acid, with a pH meter.

There is already a major problem emerging; look back at Equation 3.1 and think what will influence the *rate* of this reaction. There are three candidates—glucose, oxygen and glucose oxidase. The one that is in shortest supply will act rather like a brake on the overall reaction and determine its rate, i.e. it will be **rate-limiting**. Now, suppose a sensor such as that in Figure 3.6 was implanted subcutaneously with the intention of measuring glucose levels in the blood within the capillaries of the skin tissues. As with most such sites in the body, the levels of glucose in capillary blood would be several orders of magnitude higher than the relatively low levels of oxygen present.

▷   What is most likely to be the rate-limiting factor? How will this affect the working of the glucose sensor?

▶   Because oxygen is in short supply, it is likely to be the rate-limiting factor. (The enzyme is present in large amounts, i.e. it is present 'in excess', so it is unlikely to be rate-limiting.) The implication is that the output from the sensor will be determined by the level of oxygen, not glucose, which is clearly undesirable!

A related problem is that the level of oxygen at such a site is variable, and this will influence the signal output. One way round these problems may be to envelop the sensor in a special nylon membrane that has a higher permeability to oxygen than to glucose, thereby making the oxygen/glucose ratio at the electrode more favourable. Another option is not to use oxygen as the oxidizing agent (i.e. electron acceptor) in the glucose oxidase reaction, but to provide the enzyme with another substance that will accept electrons from glucose and transfer them to the sensor electrode. The problem remains, however, that sensor output can 'drift' for a variety of reasons—the enzyme may lose its activity with time, cells may grow around the sensor or it may become coated in protein (biocompatibility problems again!), or inflammation or infection may develop.

A range of potential uses of *implanted* glucose sensors is shown in Figure 3.7. Estimates of when such *in vivo* devices will be in routine use vary from 2 to 10 years-

Figure 3.7   Alternative potential ways of using implanted glucose sensors. Option 1 is a hypoglyc-aemia alarm, activated if blood glucose levels fall below a pre-set 'threshold' value of about $3\,\mathrm{mmol\,l^{-1}}$. Option 2 provides a continuous readout of blood glucose levels, which allows the adjustment of insulin dose. Option 3 is a long-term aim—using the sensor as input for a closed-loop system of insulin delivery.

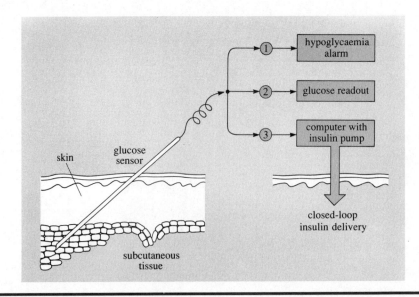

for the likes of options 1 and 2. However, *in vitro* glucose sensors present fewer technical problems and these are already in daily use, as self-monitoring instruments. For example, the instruments in Plate 3.3 are able to measure quickly and accurately glucose levels in an applied drop of blood. The details of the precise enzyme technology involved need not concern us; suffice it to say that electrons produced by the oxidation of glucose are transferred (via glucose oxidase and a mediating chemical) to the electrode. A fresh electrode is inserted prior to use, a drop of blood is applied to the target area, and the machine is switched on; in just 30 seconds a precise blood glucose value appears in a digital form on the display window.

▷   Why might this technique prove more convenient than glucose test strips (Plate 3.1)?

▶   There is no timing involved, no wiping of the sample is required and the blood glucose measurement is displayed automatically. This dispenses with the less precise method of estimating by eye the degree of colour change (though meters can now be used with glucose test strips which achieve the same end).

Patients commend this apparatus for its convenience and speed of use. It is often used in conjunction with an automatic finger-pricking device which, via a spring-loaded mechanism, fires a small lancet into the finger to produce a drop of blood. More recent innovations, again as portable and convenient as a pocket pen, allow injection of set amounts of insulin. One such syringe contains cartridges of insulin, so there is no longer the need for patients to fill up syringes from a separate insulin container prior to injection. Furthermore, the amount of insulin required can be simply 'dialed up' by altering the dose selector near the top of the pen (see Figure 3.8).

Small, hand-held computers have an increasing role in ensuring that tight control can be maintained using the convenient devices just described. Such machines are programmable by a doctor with a schedule of insulin doses specific to an individual patient. The patient subsequently enters their actual blood glucose measured periodically over a day; at any one time, the computer can quantify what insulin dose is required next. The data from the computer can be downloaded into the major computer unit at a surgery, providing an opportunity for changes in programming if an altered therapy is required. The great advantage of this form of therapy is that it allows patients the freedom to adjust their insulin treatment according to their day-to-day life-style. This is far removed from earlier methods of treatment, where the patient's life-style was dictated by the demands of therapy.

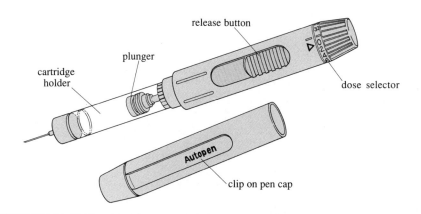

Figure 3.8 The Autopen insulin dispenser. An insulin cartridge is inserted into the cartridge holder. When the release button on the main part of the barrel is pushed down, the internal plunger moves forwards and the selected dose is delivered.

3.3 New insulins for old

3.3.1 Structure of insulin

The huge advances that have been made in the past 40 years in molecular biology and chemistry have had an enormous impact on our understanding of the structure of insulin. The fact that insulin is a protein became apparent only eight years after its discovery, but the detailed structure of the molecule remained unknown. As you know, proteins consist of chains of covalently-linked amino acids. In the case of the insulin molecule, there are two such chains: the A chain, 21 amino acids long; and the B chain of 30 amino acids. The two chains are joined together by two *disulphide bridges* (Figure 3.9). Frederick Sanger, working at the University of Cambridge, was the first to determine the amino acid sequence (the **primary structure**) of insulin. Indeed, this was the first protein for which such information became known. It was for this work that Sanger was awarded the Nobel Prize in Chemistry in 1955—in circumstances that were happily a good deal more harmonious than those accompanying the first 'insulin Nobel Prize' 32 years earlier. It is now known that the two chains are tightly coiled around each other, with the whole macromolecule folded into a tight ball; Plate 3.4 shows insulin's complex three-dimensional, **higher-order structure**.

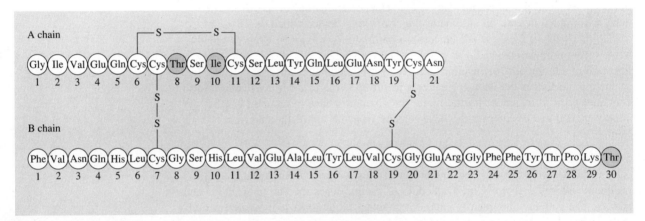

Figure 3.9 The primary structure of human insulin. The individual amino acids are identified by abbreviations, for example Gly, Phe. The identity of the amino acids, other than those shown in pink, need not concern us. Thr = threonine; Ile = isoleucine. There are three disulphide bridges (—S—S—), two of which hold the chains together.

In insulins of other species, for example those of the pig (porcine) and the cow (bovine), most of the amino acid sequence is identical to that of human insulin. But at three sites (shown in pink in Figure 3.9) the amino acids differ—Table 3.1 gives the details. Thus human and porcine insulin, for example, differ only at a single locus, B30, i.e. the last amino acid of the B chain, while bovine insulin differs from human insulin at B30 and also at A8 and A10. These sorts of differences, evident across a wide range of species, may appear trivial but in some cases can be sufficient to affect the physical properties of the molecule and, in some rare instances, its three-dimensional shape. In the examples we discuss later in this section, you will see that a difference of just one or a few amino acids has been associated with profound and most unfortunate effects for some diabetic patients.

Table 3.1 How amino acids differ at particular locations on the A and B chains in the insulins from three different species, human, pig and cow. The amino acids at other locations are all identical. Thr = threonine; Ala = alanine; Ile = isoleucine; Val = valine.

	Position on A or B chain		
	B30	A8	A10
human	Thr	Thr	Ile
porcine	Ala	Thr	Ile
bovine	Ala	Ala	Val

Figure 3.9 and Plate 3.4 show the so-called **monomeric** form of insulin, consisting of a single pair of covalently linked chains, one A and one B, but in most insulin preparations this form is comparatively rare. Monomers group together to form associations of two (*dimers*), four (*tetramers*) or six molecules (*hexamers*). When insulin is first synthesized by the pancreatic B cells, it forms hexamers in association with zinc ions (Zn^{2+}), i.e. six molecules of insulin around each Zn^{2+} ion. Multiple hexamer units can aggregate within the granules in these cells to form crystals of different shapes. After secretion from the cell, the multiple hexamers dissociate into monomers, so blood insulin is predominantly in the monomeric form.

The need to maintain glucose levels within 'tight control' over the whole day has resulted in the development of different strategies of insulin injection, often using different insulin preparations. Two basic problems exist. The first is that the rate of movement of insulin from the injection site under the skin can be variable and the other, which we mentioned in Section 2.1, is that once insulin enters the bloodstream, its effects are relatively short-lived.

Commercially available preparations now include insulin in its Zn^{2+}-associated hexameric form with protamine, a protein-like constituent that weakly binds to the insulin hexamers and so helps provide stability. This long-lasting insulin is released only slowly from the injection site so can form a useful 'background' supply of the hormone. But boosts of short-acting insulin are required to prevent the sharp elevation of blood glucose occurring after meals. The monomeric form of insulin would be the most effective for this. However, the monomers tend to clump together in solution to form dimers and tetramers (and sometimes larger aggregates) prior to and after injection, so even such 'short-acting' preparations do not have a maximum effect until about $1\frac{1}{2}$–2 hours after injection! (Figure 2.2 showed the delayed effects of injected insulin on blood glucose levels.) This means that diabetic individuals normally inject themselves about half an hour before eating, which ensures that insulin levels are already high when blood glucose concentrations begin to rise.

▷ What injection regime, combining short-acting and long-lasting insulin, might be adopted by a diabetic shift worker who sleeps during the day and has a main meal at 8.00 a.m?

▶ Short-acting insulin could be given before meals, for example about half an hour before the morning meal. Long-lasting insulins could be injected in the evening before work and again before bedtime.

▷ For what reason might a hypoglycaemic episode, i.e. a 'hypo', arise after the morning meal and how might this be prevented?

▶ Using a potent short-acting insulin, the fall in blood glucose after a meal might well be very sharp (recall Figure 2.2), so the shift worker would be well advised to eat a snack (chocolate bar or biscuit) after the morning meal before sleeping.

3.3.2 Human insulin treatment

Because animal insulins are essentially foreign proteins, they may be treated as such by the human immune system, and anti-(foreign) insulin antibodies produced in response. Such antibodies will react with the non-human insulin and sharply reduce its effectiveness. Those working in the field of diabetes had long looked forward to an era when *human* insulin would be available for routine use, but there were understandable practical and ethical problems with using human pancreatic tissue as a starting point. The human insulin era is now with us, but in controversial circumstances.

▷ From Table 3.1, how would pig insulin have to be changed to produce human insulin?

▶ Simply by replacing the B30 alanine by threonine.

This was how chemists produced the first commercially available human insulin but as you probably know, its manufacture now mostly involves recombinant DNA technology, more commonly termed genetic engineering. This procedure is now conducted commercially on a large enough scale to allow treatment of all diabetic subjects with human insulin. A variety of approaches to its manufacture is feasible — the standard procedure involves a microbe such as the bacterium *Escherichia coli*, into which a synthetic gene (that coding for the desired human protein) is inserted, using a vector such as a plasmid. For insulin, the human A and B chains are produced by separate clones of bacteria, and the two chains are afterwards joined chemically to form the functional molecule. (The description here is brief and simplistic, and you will appreciate that this is in reality a complex process.)

Only 6% of the insulin sold in the UK in 1985–86 was of the human type. But from 1986, enough recombinant human insulin was being produced to prompt the major manufacturers to wind down (though not entirely abandon) the production of porcine and bovine insulin. Their motives may have been virtuous, in part — the medical consensus was (and probably still is) that human insulin is 'better' because this is not a 'foreign' protein, which means that the development of antibodies against it is avoided. Manufacturers were also understandably concerned to capitalize on the investments they had made in this expensive new technology and to free themselves of their dependence on the supply of animal pancreases from the abbatoir. Newly-diagnosed diabetics were from then on routinely prescribed human insulin and established patients were encouraged to switch from animal insulin. By the end of 1989, more than 80% of type 1 diabetes patients in the UK were using human insulin. In countries with a strong 'green' lobby, inherently opposed to genetic engineering techniques, the adoption of human insulin has been much slower — indeed, in Germany, the opposition was sufficiently strong to prevent for some considerable time the operation of the industrial plants built to produce recombinant human insulin.

In 1987, an article was published in a major medical journal, *The Lancet*, suggesting some possible side-effects of the use of human insulin that had not come to light in clinical trials. Two Swiss doctors reported that three diabetic patients using human insulin had experienced severe hypoglycaemic episodes without prior warning symptoms. In mid-1989, a UK physician reported that in 1985 there had been 17 deaths amongst his patients who had switched to human insulin, compared to only two deaths with patients using animal insulins. His view was that such increased deaths resulted from the use of human insulin, suggesting that it reduced the all-important warning signs of imminent hypoglycaemia.

The initial Swiss report in *The Lancet* was quickly condemned by other physicians.

▷ From what you know of the Swiss report, what are its shortcomings?

▶ The sample size, three, is very small and there can be no certainty that the increased hypoglycaemia is attributable to the use of human insulin. Remember that hypoglycaemia is by no means rare in diabetics, irrespective of the form of insulin therapy used.

The editor of a leading journal on diabetes wrote a very critical rebuke to these early reports, in both title and content, claiming 'Much ado about Nothing'. He maintained that whenever a change in diabetic treatment was instigated, there was an intention to control blood glucose levels more tightly, usually with the patient's enthusiastic support. Any attempt to achieve normal glucose levels by insulin control brings an associated risk of hypoglycaemia. His own reported study failed to find any difference in the level of hypoglycaemic awareness between diabetics on human insulin and those on animal insulins. Others pointed out that the rare instances of sudden unexplained 'death in bed' of diabetic patients may not necessarily be a consequence of hypoglycaemia. Such deaths can occur in apparently healthy non-diabetic individuals; when it occurs in diabetic patients there is an unjustifiable tendency to assume that the cause must be hypoglycaemia, brought about by a particular regime or type of insulin.

But *The Lancet* report did show an interesting and familiar pattern of what has been termed 'medical me-too': the number of reported cases of hypoglycaemic unawareness with human insulin increased dramatically in the wake of the publicity! Even when more cases came to light, objective analysis of the data was difficult, partly because hypoglycaemic awareness cannot be quantified in any standard or objective way.

Then, in October 1989, a television programme highlighted, in sensational terms, the reported deaths of young diabetic patients who were using human insulin. This added extra impetus to press coverage of the issue, that was already alarmist in tone (see Figure 3.10). The British Diabetic Association was sufficiently worried by the

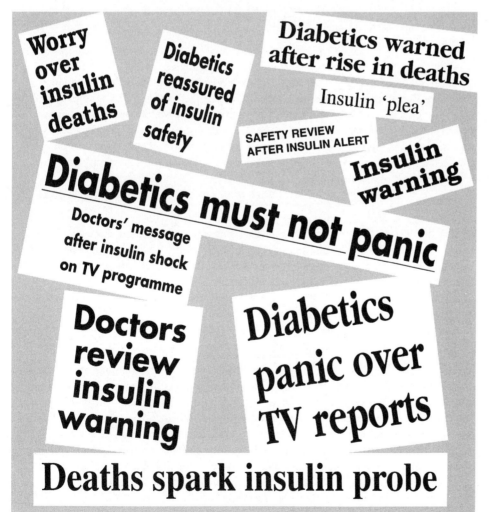

Figure 3.10 Headlines such as these, which appeared in the press between August and October 1989, understandably raised anxieties amongst Britain's diabetic patients. Recombinant human insulin was certainly under suspicion.

impact on diabetics that they issued a press release on 26 October, stressing that no type 1 diabetes patients should stop taking insulin under any circumstances. Doctors sought to reassure their patients and recommended that they keep the risks 'in proportion'; the lack of any firm scientific evidence to implicate human insulin in these deaths was emphasized. The American Diabetes Association announced that 'a loss of warning symptoms of hypoglycaemia is a complex problem that is very unlikely to be due to the type of insulin used'. Thus, for doctors and patients alike, the general picture towards the end of 1989 was confused and controversial.

Activity 3.4   *You should spend up to 20 minutes on this activity.*

Here is an opportunity to consider some of the conflicting evidence on human insulin yourself. Read through the following brief reports, (a)–(d), and write down in a couple of sentences what, if anything, it is possible to conclude from each one. Comment on the adequacy of the data where necessary and be wary about drawing *firm* conclusions.

(a) In 1989, 22 diabetic males, aged between 12 and 43 years, were discovered 'dead in bed' in the morning, having gone to bed apparently in good health the previous night. All patients were on human insulin, but only two had transferred from animal insulin within six months of their death.

(b) Of a sample of 158 diabetics who changed from bovine or porcine to human insulin, 24 stated that they had less warning of a hypoglycaemic episode. Excluded from the sample were those who altered other details of their injection regimes after switching to human insulin.

(c) Nine type 1 diabetes patients were investigated using an artificial pancreas (the Biostator; see Plate 3.2) to lower blood glucose levels, using either human or porcine insulin, in a **double-blind** procedure, i.e. neither patients nor doctors were aware of which insulin was being used. It was found that venous blood concentrations of insulin, glucagon and blood glucose changed in broadly the same way after infusion of either of the two insulins, so the responses of individual patients to human and porcine insulin could be fairly compared. In terms of hypoglycaemic awareness, eight out of nine type 1 diabetes patients felt more warning symptoms and at a higher blood glucose concentration with porcine insulin than with human insulin.

(d) Eli Lilly Research Laboratories (manufacturers of human insulin) instigated a review of data on 1 514 diabetic patients, who had recently changed to human insulin. The data were analysed for hypoglycaemic episodes, number of patients reporting lack of warning symptoms, stays in hospital and number of deaths. No statistically significant differences between any of these measures was revealed when comparing diabetics on human insulin to those on animal insulins.

The controversy is likely to persist for some time and to have a number of ramifications. What seems certain is that, for a minority of patients, the switch to human insulin causes, at the very least, changed hypoglycaemic awareness. But is this sufficient reason to be sceptical of human insulin for general use? The majority medical view is that there is 'insufficient evidence' to conclude that the change to human insulin is the cause of death in bed of diabetics, though it does accept that a minority of patients experience problems co-incident with transfer to human insulin (see Extract 3.2). Despite such reassurances, there has been intense and understandable anxiety among diabetics and their relatives (Extract 3.3).

Extract 3.2 From *The Guardian*, 10 August 1989.

Diabetes deaths and human insulin

THE British Diabetic Association is very concerned about a number of recent reports of sudden unexpected deaths of apparently healthy young people with insulin-dependent diabetes. We would like to stress that there is no evidence that these deaths are necessarily caused by hypoglycaemia or that they have anything to do with human insulin.

Sudden unexplained death in young people without diabetes is a rarity but it does occur and no satisfactory cause is found in a proportion of cases even after expert post-mortem examination. When such an unexpected death occurs in someone with diabetes, hypoglycaemia is often blamed although it is very difficult to prove conclusively because it causes no characteristic structural abnormalities and interpretation of post-mortem blood sugars is fraught with difficulty.

The problem is that after death the tissues continue to metabolize glucose for several hours so that what was a normal blood sugar at the time of death, may be within hypoglycaemic range by the time of the post-mortem.

Most young people with insulin-dependent diabetes are now treated with human insulin so that no conclusions can be drawn about whether such unexpected deaths are or are not related to human insulin. However, the BDA is aware that a minority of patients have experienced problems (particularly an attenuation or loss of the normal warning signs of a hypoglycaemic reaction) on changing from animal to human insulin. The association is pleased that the pharmaceutical companies have responded to pressure and are now placing warning statements on their human insulin packaging literature.

We would stress that nobody should have their insulin changed without a full consultation with their medical adviser and we emphasize that animal insulins are still available for those who require them. Doctors, pharmacists and patients should be aware that there might be possible effects of changing to human insulin from animal insulin and any effects should be reported to a medical adviser.

(Dr) **Robert Tattersall** (Chairman),
British Diabetic Association Professional Advisory Committee,
10 Queen Anne Street,
London W1.

Extract 3.3 From *The Guardian*, 13 August 1992.

Questions on diabetics' use of human insulin

I AM a 35-year-old diabetic, diagnosed 25 years ago and was concerned to read (July 29) of the death of a 30-year-old diabetic doctor who suffocated on her pillow due to her low blood-sugar level.

Within the last few years, insulin-dependent diabetics have been encouraged or, more to the point, told to change their insulin from the type which is extracted from animal pancreases, to 'human' insulin, a man-made insulin which has the same molecular structure as insulin produced in the human body.

Since my doctor changed me to this new insulin a few years ago, I have experienced the same problems referred to in your news report, i.e. no warning signs usually experienced when one's sugar level drops too low, quickened heart-beat, profuse sweating, numbness of the lips, etc, etc. On various occasions my blood-sugar level dropped so low that I only realised what was happening when I was on the verge of passing out. During the night

recently I was awakened by my boyfriend who was spooning honey into my mouth and talking to me, in an effort to bring me round; he had realised that my breathing pattern had changed, I was mumbling, in an extreme cold sweat and could not be roused easily. Normally, on animal insulin the early warning signals would arouse me from my sleep. I don't know what would have happened had there been no one there. I have mentioned these experiences to my doctor and to chemists both of whom have told me that other diabetics have complained of the same thing.

I have now insisted on changing back to animal insulin. Many of the insulin manufacturers have ceased making animal insulin having convinced themselves that 'human' insulin is the thing of the future, despite the opinions and wishes of diabetics themselves. I feel that the use of this new insulin should be questioned before more needless deaths occur amongst diabetics.

Felicity Lowe,
London SE13.

There are two aspects of diabetes treatment that need to be considered, which are distinct but inevitably become drawn together. First, as we have seen, tight control of blood glucose is now a daily reality for most diabetics. The driving logic behind this move has been that the medical risks that are thought to be the long-term consequence of elevated glucose levels (circulatory problems, blindness, etc.) outweigh the enhanced risks of hypoglycaemia on the intensified insulin regimes necessary to achieve tight control. The debate about whether the risks of tighter control outweigh the benefits has been rumbling on for more than 15 years. It reflects the fact that despite the enormous strides that have been made recently in our understanding of the disease, we still have a lot more to find out about the best forms of treatment.

The second area of concern is the animal/human insulin debate. This is much more recent and the circumstances surrounding the introduction of recombinant insulin have prompted questions which go much deeper than the underlying scientific issue. In scientific terms, the question is very difficult but potentially resolvable: what effect, if any, does such a very small change in insulin structure (recall Figure 3.9 and Table 3.1) have on glucose control, overall metabolism, the nervous system and therefore on hypoglycaemic awareness? We are far from an answer at present, though it is suspected there may be differences in the tendencies of various insulins to affect the nerve cells of the brain.

Secondary issues that touch on professional sensitivities and motives have a higher subjective element and inevitably cloud the scientific debate. Did patients and doctors feel encouraged to switch to human insulin by the heavy advertising from the pharmaceutical companies? Why change from animal insulin treatments which had worked well for many diabetics for many years? Were patients given appropriate information and guidance by their doctors before switching to human insulin? Were patients' concerns in the wake of a switch to human insulin taken seriously by the medical profession?

The lack of hard data and the vested interests of some of the proponents implies that this controversy too will continue for some time yet. An extra level of acrimony was guaranteed when UK lawyers stepped in to act on behalf of diabetic patients who felt they had suffered adversely from using human insulin. You will appreciate the scope for prolonged legal and scientific disagreement as you read the following extracts. Extract 3.4 seems to imply that the medical consensus is against the view that human insulins can lead to loss of hypoglycaemic awareness; while Extract 3.5 highlights two studies of diabetic patients that appear to indicate genuine differences in hypoglycaemic awareness with different types of insulin. At present, the conflict remains unresolved, but the general consensus is that there is no convincing *scientific* evidence that human insulin causes a change in hypoglycaemic awareness or increases the risk of death. The evidence that remains is largely anecdotal and subjective. In the best legal and scientific traditions, human insulin therefore stands accused but presumed innocent. With a convincing case for the defence and an insufficiently strong prosecution, it seems likely to remain so.

Extract 3.4 From the *Observer*, 29 September 1991.

Doctors accuse lawyers in row on diabetes

Annabel Ferriman
Health Correspondent

CHARGES of unethical conduct are being levelled by doctors at lawyers who are encouraging patients to sue for compensation over a new treatment for diabetes.

Solicitors are advertising in local papers, advising diabetics that if they think they suffer side-effects from the new recombinant'human' insulin they 'may well be eligible for compensation'.

Thousands of diabetics are preparing to sue Lilly Industries, the multinational company that makes human insulin, claiming it deprives them of the warning signs of a drop in sugar levels in the blood, which can result in loss of consciousness.

'In my view it is unethical', said Dr Anthony Barnett, consultant physician at East Birmingham Hospital, who cares for 3 500 diabetics. 'There is, as yet, no scientific evidence to support the hypothesis that the warning symptoms of a hypoglycaemic attack (low blood sugar level) are less good when patients are changed from animal to human insulin.'

The British Diabetic Association is so concerned about the controversy that it will announce a £100 000 task force this week to resolve the uncertainty. The controversy has prompted both sides to prepare for a legal wrangle.

Dr Barnett said there were three reasons why some diabetics might mistakenly believe the change had caused them to lose their warning signs:

o About a third of diabetics who have been insulin-dependent for more than 10 years lose their warning symptoms regardless of the type of insulin that they are on.

o In the Eighties, new inventions such as blood glucose sticks meant that patients are able to monitor their blood sugar levels more accurately and keep them down, to avoid complications of diabetes such as blindness. Low blood sugar levels, however, mean that a patient is more likely to have a hypoglycaemic attack.

o Media coverage had concentrated on anecdotal accounts from diabetics convinced there was a connection.

A spokesman for one of the firms of solicitors, who advertised widely, defended their action. 'We have had about 400 inquiries since the publicity started and no criticism of the advertisements.'

Extract 3.5 From *The Guardian*, 13 September 1991.

Doctors suggest human insulin gives less warning of blackouts

Chris Mihill
Medical Correspondent

DIABETICS who have been switched from animal to human insulin may be more at risk of blackouts, studies published today say.

Seven hundred diabetics in Britain are already planning legal action over the switch.

These blackout attacks, known as hypoglycaemia, happen when the injected insulin mops up too much sugar. A number of diabetics have said that on human insulin they get fewer warning signs, such as hunger and dizziness, so are unable to take protective measures like eating sweet things.

Two papers in the British Medical Journal give weight to the complaints, although other studies have found no difference between the two insulins.

Dr Matthias Egger and Professor Arthur Teuscher, of Berne University, and Dr George

Davey Smith, from the London School of Hygiene and Tropical Medicine, have concluded from a study of 262 Swiss diabetics that those on human insulin run more than twice the risk of hypoglycaemic attacks.

The doctors also refer to an increasing number of world-wide anecdotal reports since 1984 when human insulin was introduced.

A second study by the team looked at 44 patients who received either human or animal insulin for six weeks, and then were switched to the other type for another six weeks.

The human insulin patients were more likely to report lack of concentration and restlessness, and less likely to report hunger.

The doctors suggest a large-scale randomized trial of the two types.

3.4 The search for a cure

I regard myself now as a totally cured diabetic, so why is transplantation not being hailed as the greatest medical breakthrough since Banting and Best discovered insulin? It is a question that has been worrying me since my recovery. Each morning I wake up and marvel how well I feel. I can eat breakfast or not, a choice a diabetic can never begin to ponder in their wildest dreams. But this is when my conscience pricks me. If I can feel so well and happy with life once again, why are far more people not being offered the same opportunities as I was?

(From 'Can diabetes be cured?' by Gerry Pritchard, recipient of a pancreas transplant, in *Balance*, April/May, 1989.)

The life of this diabetic patient has been transformed since an operation that has come close to offering a cure for diabetes—**pancreatic transplantation**, i.e. transplantation of either the whole or part of the pancreas. Before the operation, he was blind and suffered from chronic kidney failure, and so had to undergo the unpleasant procedure of regular and frequent dialysis treatment. Some of the diabetes symptoms (e.g. blindness) inevitably persisted after transplantation but clearly the patient benefited enormously from the operation, so why indeed, as the patient asks, is it comparatively rare?

Pancreatic transplantation is a major surgical procedure, technically much more difficult than kidney transplantation. There are a number of digestive enzymes produced by the main bulk of the pancreas in an active form (for example, lipases—Section 2.2) that would be highly dangerous if they leaked into the recipient's body.

▷ What well-established surgical procedure might stop this secretion?

▶ Ligation of the pancreatic duct, as pioneered by Banting and Best, should lead to breakdown of tissue producing the external secretion.

Ligation does indeed seem to have this effect, but as Banting and Best found, the procedure is tricky and unreliable. Other approaches involve linking the duct of the implanted pancreas to the gut or bladder, where the external secretion would do no harm. The surgical problems, though not without risk, are largely surmountable but, even so, about 10% of recipients die within a year of the operation. The greater problem, as with all forms of organ transplantation, is the possibility of rejection. About 30% of transplants normally fail within the year, despite careful tissue matching. This is because of the production in the recipient of antibodies against 'foreign' markers on the cells of the transplanted tissue, which ultimately leads to rejection of the transplant. To counter rejection, drugs that suppress the immune system (**immuno-suppressive drugs**) are continuously prescribed. These drugs themselves have a mildly toxic effect on the insulin-producing Islet cells. Diabetics with substantial kidney failure are, however, often suitable candidates for a *double* transplant, as was the patient quoted above, because the same drugs prevent rejection of both the new kidney and the new pancreas. In these circumstances, the side-effects of such treatments may be tolerable, given the severity of their initial diabetic condition.

In the few cases so far of pancreatic transplantation from one identical twin to the other—where problems of rejection are minimized because of exact tissue matching—a separate problem becomes evident. In all cases, the diabetes of the recipients initially disappeared, only to returned within weeks.

▷ From your knowledge of the causes of diabetes, can you suggest an explanation?

▶ Remember that type 1 diabetes is likely to be an auto-immune disease, (see Section 3.1). The implication here is that the destructive factor causing the initial insulin-producing cells to stop functioning (for example, recall Activity 3.1) can persist and repeat the process.

The *potential* advantage of pancreatic transplantation goes beyond simple relief from insulin injections, diets and blood monitoring—it might arrest or even reverse some of the complications of diabetes that we have mentioned already. But most recipients will already have these complications at such an advanced stage that improvement is unlikely. By this logic, the better time for transplantation is before the severe complications develop, which means early on in diabetes. But only 40% of type 1 diabetes cases develop complications to a life-threatening stage and it is impossible to predict which patients these will be. So, if transplantation were routine, many patients would be subject to the risks of the operation and to prolonged immunosuppressive therapy, perhaps unnecessarily. For most diabetic patients, prolonged insulin therapy may be the less risky and more acceptable treatment, particularly in view of the innovations that are now available.

Some centres for pancreatic transplantation, notably in the USA, do retain an enthusiasm for the technique, but most doctors are sceptical. There is more general enthusiasm for *Islet* transplantation. The first step, now performed with an ease that Banting and Best would have been envious of, involves the separation of the hormone-producing cells of the pancreas from those producing the external secretion. Thus there is no problem of leakage of damaging enzymes and the isolated Islets can be injected through a needle to take up permanent positions in, for example, the spleen, the kidney or, in the organ that seems to give the greatest success to date— the liver. The injection of approximately 300 000 Islets appears to be required, which is just about a practical possibility, given that each human pancreas (up to now the sole source of Islets for transplantation into humans) may contain as many as 2 million of them. Remarkably, these isolated cell groups initially thrive and produce insulin (and the two other glucose-regulatory Islet hormones) at their new location; the problem is to ensure they carry on doing so long after transplantation!

Of course there still remains the problem of rejection, so this method is being pioneered—notably in the UK, USA, Italy and Canada—largely with patients receiving both Islet and kidney transplants. Despite the toxic side-effects of immunosuppressive drug treatment, at least some patients have achieved 'long-term' insulin-independence, for up to a year. If the body rejects the Islets, the transplanted cells will die. However, unlike with whole pancreatic transplantation, there is the advantage that no additional operation is required to remove transplanted Islets, because the tissue mass is sufficiently small to be broken down and reabsorbed by the body.

A number of exciting possibilities for this technique are presently being actively explored:

o Suitable Islets could perhaps be stored indefinitely in liquid nitrogen (i.e. subjected to cryopreservation), forming a suitable 'stockpile'. After thawing of the tissue, more than 80% of the Islets are viable.

o It may be possible to identify those cells of the Islets that cause rejection (by provoking antibody formation in the recipient). Perhaps these cells could be selectively destroyed prior to transplantation, for example by gamma irradiation, or coated with some neutral substance (i.e. one that does not provoke antibody formation), thereby avoiding the need for immunosuppression.

o Islets can be encapsulated within small porous tubes prior to transplantation. The pores in the walls of the tube are too small to allow entry of the components of the immune system that would attack and destroy the Islet cells, but large enough to allow the outward passage of insulin (a relatively small protein molecule). So, with this technique too, drugs to prevent rejection would not be necessary— though problems of biocompatibility remain.

At present, all these approaches are being actively researched via experimentation on animals. The problems of transferring the knowledge thereby obtained to the study of human diabetes will be significant, but not insurmountable. An imminent 'overnight' success, of a type reminiscent of Banting and Best's achievement is unlikely, but if the present rapid rate of progress is maintained, an effective 'cure' is more than likely in about 10–20 years time. Then doctors should be able to give newly-diagnosed diabetic children appropriate treatment that will make them insulin-independent for life and so free them of the long-term complications of the disease.

Summary of Chapter 3

1 Enhanced medical understanding and changes in social attitudes led to a gradual improvement in prospects for diabetics after the Second World War.

2 Two types of diabetes mellitus exist—insulin dependent (IDDM or type 1 diabetes) and non-insulin dependent (NIDDM or type 2 diabetes).

3 People with type 1 diabetes cannot survive without insulin treatment. Type 1 diabetes is a disease that arises predominantly in the young and the severe symptoms (glycosuria, thirst, weight loss) are now thought to be the culmination of diet- and/or environment-triggered, auto-immune destruction of insulin-producing Islet cells. A constituent of cow's milk (bovine serum albumin, BSA) may be implicated in provoking an immunological reaction.

4 Type 2 diabetes is the more common form of diabetes and usually affects older, more obese individuals. Such patients may benefit from insulin therapy, but they do not require it for survival. The disease involves a combination of impaired insulin secretion and reduced sensitivity of the tissues to insulin. Early nutrition, perhaps before birth, may be a critical factor in the development of type 2 diabetes.

5 Complications usually arise in both type 1 and type 2 diabetes, and are of varying severity. Malfunctions of the eyes, the kidneys, circulation and nerves can all occur, reducing life expectancy.

6 Glucagon acts antagonistically to insulin, i.e. it elevates blood glucose levels and promotes glycogen breakdown. Insulin and glucagon are only two of several hormones that contribute to blood glucose control and they do so in a complex way, which is difficult to simulate in the treatment of diabetics.

7 Current medical consensus favours maintaining blood glucose levels close to normal values, i.e. tight control is advocated, even though this may increase the likelihood of hypoglycaemia.

8 Continuous subcutaneous insulin infusion (CSII) achieves tight control by post-meal boosts supplementing basal infusion. Fully implantable pumps are in the research and development phase, though considerable problems of pump technology and of biocompatibility remain.

9 Most glucose sensors utilize the enzyme glucose oxidase, for example those now used in routine self-monitoring. A long-term goal is to include such a sensor within a closed-loop system of insulin delivery, relying on negative feedback to regulate insulin infusion. A large, complex artificial pancreas is already available but is usable at present only for hospitalized patients.

10 Of the range of insulins now available for therapy, human insulin is the most widely used, usually manufactured by recombinant DNA technology. There is evidence of reduced hypoglycaemic awareness in some patients who have been newly

prescribed human insulin, but there is controversy about its frequency and cause. Unexplained deaths among diabetic patients cannot be ascribed with any certainty to the use of human insulin.

11 Pancreatic transplantation approaches being a 'cure' for diabetes. The technique can sometimes prevent patients developing severe complications. Surgical risks, as well as rejection and further auto-immune destruction, are inherent disadvantages of 'whole pancreas' transplantation that, for most patients, outweigh potential benefits. Islet transplantation offers the best hope for insulin-independence, and carries fewer associated risks.

12 Recent advances in technology (for example, pen injection and finger-pricking devices) have further aided effective 'self-help' in patients, i.e. achieving tighter control with greater patient responsibility. Hand-held computers are likely to be increasingly used in supporting patients in the management of their diabetes.

Question 3.1 Identify each of the following as (i) characteristic of type 1 diabetes, (ii) characteristic of type 2 diabetes or (iii) characteristic of both types of diabetes.

(a) Poor control of blood glucose levels.

(b) Reduced sensitivity of tissues to insulin.

(c) Symptoms of thirst and high urine output.

(d) Complications can ensue, for example kidney damage.

(e) Always requires insulin to achieve blood glucose control.

Question 3.2 Identify each of the following as matters of (i) fact or (ii) opinion/controversy.

(a) Insulin and glucagon act antagonistically.

(b) Use of human insulin often reduces hypoglycaemic awareness.

(c) Human insulin is chemically different from both porcine and bovine insulin.

(d) Animal insulins reduce human blood glucose levels.

(e) Islet cell transplantation offers the best prospect of a 'cure'.

Question 3.3 There have been cases of murder by insulin injection. What features should be looked for at the post-mortem?

Question 3.4 Those questioning the use of animals in research have asserted that the importance of the discovery of insulin has been exaggerated. They claim that the incidence of deaths from diabetes in modern times is little different from that of the pre-Banting and Best era. How might such data be explained, assuming they were valid?

Question 3.5 Which of the following descriptions relate to (i) the Biostator, (ii) the CSII device and (iii) a glucose sensor?

(a) Infusion of insulin at a steady basal rate, supplement by meal-time boosts, triggered by the patient.

(b) Automatic adjustments of the amount of insulin infused into the blood, depending on blood glucose content.

(c) A miniature probe, involving a reaction catalysed by glucose oxidase, which can potentially be used *in vivo* or *in vitro*.

(d) Creates risks of infection and of 'biocompatibility'.

(e) Is implanted fully into the body.

Extract 3.6 From *The Guardian*, 30 August 1991.

Diabetics' insulin action

Lawyers representing hundreds of diabetics who suffered side-effects after their animal-derived insulin was switched to a laboratory-made product yesterday set up a steering committee to deal with an expected flood of negligence claims.

Activity 3.5

A brief newspaper report (Extract 3.6) prompted a letter on the subject of human insulin (Extract 3.7). Read both extracts carefully and then answer the following questions.

(a) What comments do you have on the accuracy of Extract 3.6?

(b) To what does Wolff (in Extract 3.7) attribute the 'complications' of diabetes?

(c) Does Wolff believe that human insulin reduces hypoglycaemic awareness?

(d) Compose a brief letter of response putting the alternative point of view to that of Wolff.

Extract 3.7 From *The Guardian*, 2 September 1991.

Human insulin: the gap between opinion and fact

PLAINTIFFS in the proposed lawsuit of manufacturers of human insulin (Guardian, August 30) allege that human insulin makes them more likely to suffer potentially life-threatening lowering of blood sugar levels than when they are treated with animal insulin. The case will allow examination of interesting issues in diabetic patient care.

Diabetes is characterized initially by stark increases in blood sugar. The disease is, however, often followed by the 'diabetic complications'; blindness, heart disease, as well as nerve and kidney damage which shorten life and make it more miserable. Nobody really knows what causes this later organ failure. It has, however, become accepted medical opinion that it is somehow caused by high sugar levels. Diabetic patients are thus urged to keep their blood sugar levels as close to normal as possible.

There is, however, a wide gap between the medical opinion that high blood sugar is 'toxic' and objective medical and scientific evidence. It now seems increasingly unlikely that high blood sugar is responsible for the tissue damage which afflicts the diabetic. But when diabetic patients keep their blood sugar very tightly regulated this alone makes them less aware of dangerously low blood sugar. In effect, they appear to be exposed to risk and thus potentially damaged by their therapy.

It is unfortunate that the widespread adoption of an inappropriate policy of strict control of blood sugar coincided with the useful introduction of human insulin. It would be doubly unfortunate if human insulin became the scapegoat on which all adverse effects of the ill-judged policy were conveniently blamed.

Simon P. Wolff,
Lecturer in Toxicology,
Dept of Clinical Pharmacology,
University College and Middlesex School of Medicine.

4 Looking ahead; future promise

As we stand, Islet transplant technique is not good enough. For years people tried to do kidney transplants and failed. They knew that it was related to rejection, but nobody had a way of overcoming it. Then there were some minor advances which made kidney transplants work for a short period, a bit longer than Islet transplants do now. But then, out of the blue, we suddenly came up with a drug that allowed you to put transplants in and control the rejection. Within three years everybody was doing kidney transplants. And they were working! So that is the kind of advance that can occur, although there's no predicting it.

(A quote from Dr David Gray, a leading researcher in Islet transplantation, in 'The quest for a cure' by Lesley Hallett, in *Balance*, August/September, 1990.)

This quote illustrates that future progress in the field of diabetes is certain, but that neither its direction nor its effects are predictable. The pace of research is now very brisk and the prospects for diabetic patients never better. Advances in understanding the biological basis of diabetes have been hand-in-hand with the development of new technologies—glucose test strips, implantable insulin pumps, recombinant human insulin.

Genetic engineering techniques have great potential for future insulin therapy. Synthetic genes can be produced that code for proteins very similar in structure and function to human insulin but with chosen specific differences in amino acid sequence. Theoretically, a huge variety of such insulin-like molecules can be designed. One aim of this work is to produce 'customized insulins' that will exert the same effects on target cells as conventional insulins but have the important advantage that they remain active in the body for longer periods. The genetically engineered long-lasting insulin-like molecules that are currently being developed include the following broad types:

1 Those with enhanced lipid solubility. The 'insulin'–lipid solution could be injected, or inserted as a 'mini-implant', and the 'insulin' would diffuse out into the bloodstream continuously and at a predictable rate.

2 Those that are *not* taken into the target cell and destroyed after binding to the receptor and exerting their effect, but are released and can then bind to other receptors. (Such molecules have a modified amino acid sequence at the receptor binding site—Plate 3.4.)

Innovations such as these are likely to have an increasing day-to-day effect on those with diabetes, at least in the developed countries. There are opportunities for further major improvements in the management of the disease from many areas of research:

o Perhaps a synthetic compound that will mimic the effects of insulin but, unlike insulin, can be taken orally.

o Perhaps new understanding about one of the other hormones implicated in diabetes (there is currently great interest in *another*—recently discovered—B cell hormone, called amylin).

o Perhaps the development of a diabetes vaccine (remember that viral infection may be an initial trigger—Activity 3.1)

o Perhaps improved methods of insulin delivery.

There are two, related, points that have a special importance; each indicates how long is the difficult road towards full understanding and control of diabetes.

First, the prospects of a cure for diabetes look good in the long term. But delights in the progress of the past should not blind us to the enormous problems that remain to be solved. Islet transplantation is a good example. Once the technique has been perfected, and this is surely only a matter of time, medical science will once again bring about a dramatic and welcome revolution in the treatment of diabetes. But we will first need to establish that there are no long-term consequences of cell transplantation—for example, might the technique increase the likelihood of local tumours developing?

Secondly, increased understanding of the causes of diabetes will bring enormous benefits but also dilemmas and difficulties. Even now it is possible to identify particular genetic features (called *markers*) of individuals who are susceptible to type 1 diabetes. Even with our current knowledge and technology it would be theoretically feasible to conduct a large-scale screening programme that would identify individuals most likely to develop type 1 diabetes on the basis of such markers, or predict which relatives of existing type 2 diabetics are likely to develop the disease. It is also possible to detect the antibodies that indicate that the process of Islet-cell destruction has begun and so identify the individuals in whom diabetes is imminent.

But what purpose would be served by this if at such a time diabetes could not be prevented or cured? Also remember that genetic markers identify individuals that are *susceptible* to the disease, not those who are certain to develop it. Here the long-term medical advantages of improved understanding of the disease have to be weighed against the psychological anxiety at the level of the individual. Knowledge can be uncomfortable, especially if accompanied by uncertainty.

It seems fitting to end by quoting from the final section of Michael Bliss' book *The Discovery of Insulin*. Here he neatly brings together the two eras, of discovery and then development, that have been the focus of our attention in this book:

> *Hundreds of researchers, spending millions of dollars every year, are working on all of the questions related to diabetes and insulin. The difference between the world-wide research effort of the 1980s and that of 1921–23 in Toronto is like that between the exploration of space and the flight at Kitty Hawk in 1903. Nameless astronauts now fly space shuttles; the Wright brothers won the immortality. The immortality of the discoverers of insulin was particularly deserved, in the sense that for diabetics it was much more than a matter of just getting a new hormone off the ground. All the later questions, all the current ones, are secondary to the one answered in 1921–22 at Toronto. With insulin, the stone was rolled away, and diabetes became a matter of life, not death.*

Further reading

Advances in the treatment of diabetes are frequently covered in the 'serious' press and in science magazines such as *New Scientist*. Practical information on diabetes is available from the British Diabetic Association, at 10 Queen Anne Street, London W1M 0BD. The association's publication *Balance* (from which we have quoted twice in this book) is a good source of information, as is the journal *Practical Diabetes*.

Should you be interested in reading more about the contents of Chapters 2 and 3, the following books are recommended.

Ashcroft, F. M. and Ashcroft, S. J. H. (1992) *Insulin*, IRL Press (OUP), Oxford.
This book reviews current knowledge about insulin, from the mechanism of its synthesis to the complications of diabetes. It is aimed principally at graduate students and research workers. However, the authors assert that each major area is introduced in a way that can be understood by readers who have no prior knowledge of the field.

Bliss, M. (1988) *The Discovery of Insulin*, Faber and Faber, London.
This is an enthralling and beautifully written account of the events at the University of Toronto in 1921–22 and their aftermath and has been the major source for Chapter 2. Reading it would provide a much fuller picture of both the scientific discovery itself and the attendant clashes of personalities. Well worth buying.

Pickup, J. and Williams, G. (1992) *Textbook of Diabetes*, Blackwells, Oxford.
This expensive two-volume publication is a multi-author treatise for reference rather than detailed reading. It contains over one hundred articles on specific aspects of diabetes, many covered only fleetingly in Chapter 3, e.g. implantable pumps, the epidemiology (occurrence) of diabetes, anti-insulin antibodies. Mainly written for a medical audience, but accessible by non-specialists too.

Sönksen, P., Fox, C. and Judd, S. (1991) (2nd edn) *Diabetes at Your Fingertips*, Class Publishing, Knightsbridge, London.
This is a comprehensive but very accessible diabetes 'reference book', designed to enable patients to 'learn about their diabetes', with 450 clear and accurate answers to common questions.

Skills

In this section we list skills that have been explicitly taught and/or revised in this book. You should find that most of them are special instances of the general skill categories listed in the *Course Study Guide*. Some are new (7 and 8) and are linked explicitly with the content of this book, but others have been practised in earlier books.

1   Describe or interpret data, including experimental results, presented as text, graphs and diagrams. (*Activities 2.2, 2.3, 3.1, 3.3 and 3.4*)

2   Summarize, in writing or in the form of a flow chart, the main points from a section of text that you have studied. (*Activities 2.1 and 3.2*)

3   Extract from an article, information that is relevant to a particular question, and by integrating that information with what you already know, give an answer to the question in your own words. (*Question 3.3; Activity 3.5*)

4   Distinguish between correlations and causal relationships. (*Activity 3.4*)

5   Consider social, political and ethical aspects of a scientific issue. (*Question 3.4; Activity 3.5*)

6   Formulate a personal opinion on a scientific issue. (*Activity 2.4*)

7   Consider how an interplay of scientific and personal concerns can prompt or hinder the process of scientific discovery, with the result that credit for a discovery can be difficult to apportion. (*Activity 2.4*)

8   Demonstrate an understanding of how scientific knowledge and improved technology can be applied for better disease management. (*Activities 3.4 and 3.5*)

Answers to questions

Question 2.1

Only (a) is correct—remember that insulin lowers blood glucose levels because it stimulates cells to take up more glucose; muscle and liver (and fat too) are particularly important in this respect.

The discussion of Figure 2.1 showed that insulin is produced at sites distinct from those involved in the production of digestive enzymes, so (b) is incorrect.

Your flow chart from Activity 2.1 should remind you that *raised* glucose levels prompt insulin release; negative feedback switches release off when normal glucose levels are restored ((c) incorrect).

Looking back at Figures 2.2 and 2.3 should convince you that (d) is incorrect. Insulin levels in the blood fall as normal glucose levels are restored, for reasons mentioned in Section 2.1. (The fact that the effects of insulin 'wear off' a few hours after injection is only too well appreciated by diabetics.) It is also not really justifiable, on the evidence of Figure 2.2, to state that insulin has an effect *immediately*—we shall say more about this in Chapter 3.

Question 2.2

The correct sequence is (e), (b), (d), (c), (f), and (a).

The high sugar content of the urine of diabetics (e) was known by ancient physicians. Paul Langerhans identified the Islets in 1869 (b). They were implicated as the sites of internal secretion soon after Minkowski's experiments (d); at a later date (1916), the term insulin was first employed (c). Banting was the first to inject degenerate pancreas into diabetics (f), though Minkowski, Paulesco and Kleiner had all tried extracts of fresh pancreas. The therapeutic use of insulin (a) was first accomplished using Collip's extract.

Question 2.3

(d) is the most accurate description. As you know, the idea of ligating the duct and using the 'degenerate' pancreas was unnecessary, but it did have the virtue of setting the Toronto group onto a productive line of investigation, if not the methodologically 'correct' one. These early experiments convinced them that they were seeing the effects of an active internal secretion, the extraction of which became the object of their attention.

(a) is incorrect—Section 2.2.2 makes it clear that insulin is present in extracts of *fresh* pancreas, when appropriately treated.

(b) is incorrect—the demonstration was not fully *conclusive*, as the answer to Activity 2.3 indicated.

(c) is incorrect—the internal secretion from the degenerate pancreas was heavily contaminated, and its injection prompted an adverse reaction (Section 2.2.2).

Question 3.1

(a) (iii); (b) (ii); (c) (iii); (d) (iii); (e) (i).

Note from Section 3.1 that both type 1 and type 2 diabetic patients have poor control over blood glucose levels, so with respect to (a) the two conditions are similar. For this reason, type 2 patients have to restrict their carbohydrate intake and sometimes take drugs that have a hypoglycaemic affect. The symptoms are much the same (see (c)), except that type 2 patients usually show no sudden weight loss, and complications can ensue with both (d). By definition, type 1 diabetes requires insulin treatment (e), and type 2 diabetes patients usually have reduced tissue sensitivity (b), probably because of changes in insulin–receptor binding.

Question 3.2

(a) (i); (b) (ii); (c) (i); (d) (i); (e) (ii).

So, in my opinion, (a), (c) and (d) are matters of established fact, whereas both (b) and (e) are matters of opinion, as Sections 3.3 and 3.4 indicated.

Question 3.3

Knowledge of insulin action would suggest that there should be low levels of glucose in the blood, i.e. hypoglycaemia, together with unusually high levels of stored glycogen (e.g. in the liver). You might also expect there to be unusually high levels of insulin.

Extract 3.2 described what actually happens, which is that, after death (even when due to natural causes) glucose levels in the blood fall very sharply, because of continued metabolic breakdown (i.e. glycolysis) after death. It is therefore far from easy to diagnose hypoglycaemia at post-mortem.

Question 3.4

First, the incidence of deaths from diabetes would have to be expressed as a rate per head of population, which takes account of the fact that the world's population has doubled over the past half-century. In addition, the age of diabetics at death has to be considered. Death from diabetes does of course still occur, but usually at an age much closer to average life expectancy.

Note too that because genetic factors are implicated in diabetes—especially type 2— the incidence is likely to increase as more diabetic patients reproduce. (Formerly, many diabetics did not live long enough to reproduce.) Finally, as Extract 3.1 pointed out, unknown environmental and/or dietary factors appear to be having an increasing effect in triggering the disease.

Question 3.5

(a) (ii); (b) (i); (c) (iii); (d) (i), (ii) and (iii); (e) none of (i)–(iii)—this description only applies to the fully implantable insulin pump.

Answers to activities

Activity 2.1

Your flow chart should include all the stages shown in Figure 2.7, although the precise wording you use will probably be different from that in the figure.

The negative feedback is best represented by an arrow drawn from the final box acting 'upstream' and influencing the release of insulin. Remember that the restoration of normal blood sugar levels 'turns off' the secretion of insulin (except for the continuous basal secretion). Note that this feedback arrow (red in Figure 2.7) completes a loop in the system, which explains the relevance of the term 'closed-loop control'.

This feedback arrow needs to be distinguished in some way from the other arrows in the flow chart, which mean 'leads to' or 'stimulates'. In Figure 2.7, a thick vertical bar at the end of the arrow indicates the process of inhibition. (This is how a feedback loop would normally be represented in physiological control mechanisms of this type.)

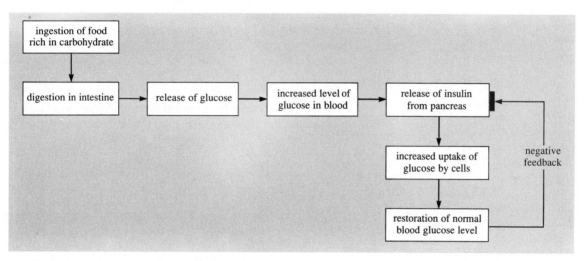

Figure 2.7 Answer to Activity 2.1.

Activity 2.2

(a) Breakfast would have been at about 8.00 a.m. and lunch at about noon, i.e. before the start of significant blood glucose increases. Note that even in a non-diabetic individual, with good control of blood glucose, eating is likely to lead to temporary elevations in blood glucose level. During fasting periods, i.e. between meals, blood glucose levels move up and down 'spontaneously', e.g. at around 16.00 in Figure 2.2.

(b) Increased insulin secretion is likely to have begun soon after eating breakfast and again soon after eating lunch. The clue was provided in the text; insulin is released immediately when glucose levels are raised. (It is difficult to be any more precise about the timing, because blood glucose measurements are taken only at hourly intervals. It actually takes about half an hour after eating for digestion to be sufficiently complete to cause an increase in blood glucose level and a consequent increase in insulin secretion.)

(c) Perhaps the meal was very light. Even a sizeable meal might not have much effect on blood glucose if it was very low in carbohydrate.

(d) Yes. Prior to the injection of insulin, there is no effective mechanism in the diabetic individual to remove glucose from the bloodstream, so average blood glucose levels are higher. For the same reason, blood glucose levels in the diabetic individual rise dramatically after a meal, whereas in the non-diabetic individual, the rise is much more modest and 'pre-meal' levels are eventually restored.

(e) Just like the body's own insulin, the injected insulin stimulates the cells of responsive tissues, notably those of the liver and muscles, to take up glucose from the blood; to be stored in such tissues in the form of glycogen.

(i) In the diabetic individual, injected insulin can take some time to have its full effect—on the evidence of Figure 2.2, more than an hour. This is the reason why diabetic patients normally inject themselves with insulin *before* a meal, not after a meal as in the figure. The timings of injections in Figure 2.2 were chosen to show the dramatic rise in blood glucose levels that occur after eating if there is insufficient insulin present.

(ii) A fall in blood sugar is particularly striking after injection A, where the insulin dose is actually so large that there is a danger of hypoglycaemia. A smaller dose (for example, B) fails to restore blood sugar levels to 'normal' values and the patient remains hyperglycaemic. The data show both the importance and the difficulty of getting the insulin dose for diabetics 'just right', about which we will say more in Chapter 3.

Activity 2.3

(a) Because of the need to establish that blood sugar levels were stable before the injection of the extract. Unless you did so, you could not be sure that it was the effects of the extract that had brought about a change in levels. Figure 2.2 showed that blood glucose levels normally move up and down spontaneously. Here, stability of blood sugar levels is assumed on the basis of two measurements prior to injection!

(b) Not really. It is indeed true that blood sugar level falls after each injection but the effect appears to be transitory—blood sugar level actually *increased* prior to death. However, the dog was clearly very ill, and it is possible that the observed changes in blood sugar levels after injection would have occurred anyway prior to death.

(c) There are a variety of possible approaches. First, you could try to obtain a purer extract and measure body temperature to see if it still rises after injection of the extract. If it does not and yet blood glucose levels fall, this suggests that the fall is due to the effects of the extract and not to fever. Alternatively, one could inject a drug that would prevent any elevation of temperature during the experiment, then administer the extract and look for any change in blood glucose levels (or simply keep the dog cool, throughout). Another approach is to inject a drug that brings on fever without injecting extract and look for any change in the level of glucose in the urine.

(d) The total volume of extract injected was a very small proportion of the blood volume (less than 2%) and so dilution alone could not possibly account for the observed 40% reduction in blood glucose (from 0.5 to 0.3 g%).

(e) No! Remember that Banting's original hypothesis was that the effectiveness of the internal secretion could be maintained during its extraction only if spared from the effects of the external secretion. But here was an extract of whole pancreas (therefore containing the external secretion) that had the same effect as extracts from degenerate pancreas, which Banting supposed lacked functional digestive-enzyme-producing cells.

Activity 2.4

(a) There is no easy answer here! My first thoughts are as follows: Banting was the prime mover behind the early work and without him the discovery of insulin would almost certainly have been delayed. Best did much of the routine work, though the ideas seemed to stem mainly from Banting. Both Macleod and Collip made important contributions.

The answers to (b) and (c) hold the key.

(b) The simple answer is that Macleod provided the facilities that Banting needed, in terms of laboratory space, and support, in the form of Best. But despite Banting's claims to the contrary, Macleod did much more than this—remember from Section 2.2.1 that he helped with the initial surgical techniques and then, more significantly, he offered critical help and guidance to Banting and Best, although this was often ignored.

(c) To Collip goes the credit for producing the first reasonably pure insulin extract that could be used safely on diabetic patients. This is something that Banting and Best had failed to do, because they were ignorant of the important chemical 'tricks of the trade'. This was the key feature of Collip's work in Toronto that set it apart from that of others (such as Kleiner) who had tried out pancreatic extracts on diabetics.

Activity 3.1

On the evidence presented here, the onset of type 1 diabetes appears to be linked with bottle-feeding (item 2), in particular with the absorption of BSA (item 1). In susceptible individuals, levels of anti-BSA antibodies are raised (item 4). Such antibodies can react 'inappropriately' with p69 (item 5). When susceptible individuals suffer one or more viral infections, p69 levels on the surface of insulin-producing cells are enhanced (item 3) and these cells are therefore killed (item 6).

Activity 3.2

My suggestions are as follows:

1 The incidence of diagnosis of type 1 diabetes in the UK and the Irish Republic has doubled in the last 15 years, and is now at an annual rate of 13.5 per 100 000 children under 15. (You may also have mentioned the increased proportion of type 1 diabetes in under-fives—raised from 19 to 25%.)

2 There are geographical differences in incidence in the UK; e.g. Scotland and the North of England have higher than average values, and in Ireland and London values are lower than average.

3 There are much greater variations in incidence internationally—values range from 1.7 cases per 100 000 in Japan to 28.6 cases per 100 000 in Finland, with the British Isles approximately in the middle of this range. (Note that the existence of such variation was hinted at in Activity 3.1, item 2; it is worth noting in passing that Finland has one of the highest per capita consumptions of cow's milk and Japan one of the lowest.)

Perhaps you condensed points 2 and 3 by stating more simply that, in general, the further north a country or region lies, the higher the incidence of diabetes.

Another new item of information you may have included is that the earlier type 1 diabetes develops, the greater the chance that complications such as blindness or kidney disease will occur.

Activity 3.3

(a) Glycogen is a polymer of glucose, and is stored in the muscles and liver (see Section 2.1). Glucagon stimulates glycogen breakdown, releasing glucose. In contrast, as Collip first revealed (see Section 2.2.2), insulin promotes the *formation* of glycogen from glucose.

(b) This implies that glucagon is normally released when levels of glucose in the blood are low. This is consistent with (a), because glucagon would elevate blood glucose levels, returning them to near normal. The fact that glucagon secretion eventually diminishes suggests that it is subject to negative feedback control, as is the secretion of insulin (Section 2.1).

(c) This suggests that the level of one hormone (in this case insulin) has an effect on the rate of release of the other, glucagon. As you would predict from (a), the release of glucagon in such circumstances causes an increase in blood glucose levels, i.e. it has a hyperglycaemic effect. This observation also confirms that glucagon is released in response to low blood glucose levels (see (b)); prolonged exercise or starvation can each lead to a lowering of blood glucose.

Activity 3.4

Firm conclusions here are difficult, partly because a number of related phenomena are being considered under different circumstances.

(a) There is no information on whether this is an unusually high incidence of diabetic death in bed compared to previous years. Neither is there any certainty that these deaths are a result of hypoglycaemia. Remember too that hypoglycaemia is a risk with all insulin therapies. The fact that only two such deaths occurred soon after switching to human insulin may suggest some other cause of death; alternatively, it may be that the effects of a switch to human insulin are evident only after a delay of 6 months or so.

(b) It was important to exclude patients from this comparison whose changes in treatment had involved more than a switch to human insulin. The fact that only a minority of patients (about 15%) had reported some degree of loss of hypoglycaemic awareness does not mean that the phenomenon is not real, only that a minority of patients are affected.

(c) This implies that under strictly controlled conditions, human insulin *does* cause altered hypoglycaemic awareness, here in the great majority of patients. Note the important point is that neither patient nor doctor was aware of which insulin type was being administered, which was not true of many other trials. Not only was there loss of awareness (i.e. patients felt *more* symptoms with porcine insulin) but as glucose levels were lowered, the symptoms of hypoglycaemia first become apparent on porcine insulin at a higher blood glucose concentration than with human insulin. In other words, the threshold at which symptoms first become evident may be different for different insulins; with human insulin the threshold is *lower*.

(d) Unlike the physiological measurement mentioned in (c), these data rely on analysing past experiences of diabetics established on different insulin types. Here no differences were reported, but given the difficulties of proving a negative, this always leaves room for doubt. Some critics may be inherently suspicious of research work conducted by or on behalf of a major manufacturer of human insulin, but others would argue that it would be in the best (long-term) interests of the company to uncover any evidence of the adverse effects of human insulin.

Activity 3.5

(a) The phrase 'laboratory-made' is unhelpful. All insulins are in some sense laboratory-made, even when simply extracted from animal tissue. What should have been made clear is that the insulin in question is human insulin, manufactured by recombinant DNA techniques.

(b) Wisely, he refrains from doing so, stating that 'nobody really knows what causes this later organ failure'.

(c) No, though he is a little equivocal on the point. He inclines to the view that tighter control of blood glucose levels is the most likely explanation of increased incidence of hypoglycaemia.

(d) I felt this was a difficult undertaking! My own view is that Wolff's arguments are persuasive, but since I was required to adopt a contrary view, in gladiatorial style, my first attempt 'off the cuff' was:

> *Wolff fails to take into account that large numbers of diabetics, who have long practised tight control of their blood glucose levels, have reported reduced hypoglycaemic awareness after switching to human insulin, while keeping all other aspects of their insulin control unchanged. This implies that a minority of patients do indeed have a sensitivity to human insulin, for reasons as yet unknown. Furthermore, carefully-controlled 'double-blind' experiments have revealed that patients injected with human insulin do have different and reduced hypoglycaemic symptoms from those injected with animal insulin.*

Here I am calling on information in Activity 3.4, but you may have included points from Extracts 3.3 and 3.5, though I feel item 3 in Activity 3.4 is the stronger evidence.

Notice how easy it is to fall into the trap of bending the facts to suit one's own purpose and ignoring those that don't fit. For example, is it fair for me to claim that 'large numbers of diabetics' have reported thus? Activity 3.3 refers to 'only' 158 individuals. Also, I have little evidence for claiming 'long-practised tight control'. Can I really be sure that 'all other aspects of their insulin control were unchanged'? Note too that I have ignored evidence that doesn't support my case (see item 4 of Activity 3.3).

Reflect on your own letter and attempt the same degree of critical analysis.

Acknowledgements

The Course Team would like to acknowledge the help and advice of Dr Anne Clark of the Diabetes Research Laboratories, Radcliffe Infirmary, Oxford, who kindly offered comments on early drafts of the text. We also thank Dr Jonathan Levy of the Diabetes Research Laboratories for his constructive comments as external assessor for the book. We also acknowledge the help of the British Diabetic Association, especially Venessa Hebditch and Claire Stammer.

Grateful acknowledgement is made to the following sources for permission to reproduce material in this book:

Text

Extract 3.1 Mihill, C. (1991), 'Cases of child diabetes double', *The Guardian*, 22 February 1991; *Extract 3.2* Tattersall, R. (1989), 'Diabetes deaths and human insulin', *The Guardian*, 10 August 1989, © Dr Robert Tattersall, London; *Extract 3.3* Lowe, F. (1992), 'Questions on diabetics' use of human insulin', *The Guardian*, 13 August 1992, © F. Lowe; *Extract 3.4* Ferriman, A. (1991), 'Doctors accuse lawyers in row on diabetes', *The Observer*, 29 September 1991; *Extract 3.5* Mihill, C. (1991), 'Doctors suggest human insulin gives less warning of blackouts', *The Guardian*, 13 September 1991; *Extract 3.6* 'Diabetics insulin action', *The Guardian*, 30 August 1991; *Extract 3.7* Wolff, S. (1991), 'Human insulin: the gap between opinion and fact', *The Guardian*, 2 September 1991, © Simon P. Wolff.

Figures

Figures 2.4, 2.6 and 3.1 British Diabetic Association; *Figure 2.5* Adapted from Bliss, M. (1988), *The Discovery of Insulin*, Macmillan Press Ltd; *Figure 3.2* Graseby Medical Ltd, Watford; *Figure 3.3* Pickup, J. (1991), 'Continuous subcutaneous insulin infusion (CSII)', in Pickup, J. and Williams, G. (eds), *Textbook of Diabetes*, Blackwell Scientific Publications Ltd; *Figure 3.4* Siemens Medical Engineering, Caversham, Reading; *Figure 3.8* Owen Mumford Ltd, Oxford. *Figures 3.6 and 3.7* Pickup, J. (1991), 'Glucose sensors', in Pickup, J. and Williams, G. (eds), *Textbook of Diabetes*, Blackwell Scientific Publications Ltd;

Colour Plates

Plate 2.1a Drs Anne E. Bishop and Julia M. Polak, Royal Postgraduate Medical School, London; *Plate 2.1b* Dr Anne Clark, Diabetes Research Laboratories, Radcliffe Infirmary, Oxford; *Plates 2.1c and d* Dr Alan Foulis, Department of Pathology, Glasgow University; *Plate 3.1* Boehringer Mannheim UK; *Plate 3.2* Prof. A. M. Albisser, Department of Medicine, Toronto University; *Plate 3.3* MediSense Britain Ltd, Birmingham; *Plate 3.4* Dr Alasdair McCleod, BioFabric and Dr Stephen Wood, Birkbeck College, London.

Index

Note: Entries in **bold** are key terms. Page numbers in *italics* refer to figures, tables and colour plates.